# A COLLECTION OF SHORT STORIES AND NON-FICTION

Edited by Mike Royston

www.heinemann.co.uk

✓ Free online support
✓ Useful weblinks
✓ 24 hour online ordering

**01865 888080**

Selection, introduction and activities by Mike Royston

**In-house team**
Publisher: Ben Hulme-Cross
Managing editor: Melissa Okusanya
Design: Georgia Bushell
Production: Jamie Copping
Picture research: Liz Alexander

Typeset by 🕭 Tek-Art, Croydon, Surrey
Cover design by Forepoint
Printed in China by CTPS Ltd
Cover photo: © Bloomimage/Corbis

**Acknowledgements**

'You Can't Bring That In Here' by Robert Swindells, from *Snake on a Bus*, published by Methuen Children's
Books. Text Copyright © Robert Swindells, Illustrations Copyright © Brett Hudson. Reprinted with
permission of Jennifer Luithlen Agency on behalf of Robert Swindells and Brett Hudson; Extract of text and
illustrations from *Stories of Toilets and Other Useful Inventions* by permission of Usborne Publishing, 83–85
Saffron Hill, London EC1N 8RT, UK www.usborne.com Copyright © 2004 Usborne Publishing Ltd; Extract of
text and illustrations from *The Best Ever Sleepover Fun Book* by Janet Hoggarth, published by Puffin 2005,
Copyright Janet Hoggarth 2005. Reprinted with permission of Penguin Books Ltd; 'The Strap Box Flyer' by
Paul Jennings, from *Unreal!* published by Penguin Australia. Reprinted with permission of Penguin
Australia; Extract from *The Pinballs* by Betsy Byars, published by Bodley Head. Copyright © 1977 by Betsy
Byars. Reprinted with permission of The Random House Group Limited and HarperCollins Publishers, USA;
'The Short History of Brian Beck' by Rony Robinson, from *Down Your Way* © Rony Robinson. Reprinted by
permission of PFD on behalf of Rony Robinson www.pfd.co.uk; Extract from *Braveheart: The Diary of A
Nine Year Old Girl who Refused to Die* by Joanne Gillespie, published by Century Hutchinson 1989.
Reprinted with permission of the MBA Literary Agency; Extract of text and illustrations from *The
Knowledge: Crashing Computers*, text copyright © Michael Coleman, 1999 illustrations copyright © Mike
Phillips 1999. Published by Scholastic Children's Books. Reproduced by permission of Scholastic. All
Rights Reserved; Text and illustrations from 'The Amazing Talking Pig' by Mick Gowar, originally published
in *The Amazing Talking Pig and Other Stories* by Mick Gowar, published by Hamish Hamilton 1993 Puffin
1994 text copyright © Mick Gowar illustrations copyright © Anni Axworthy. Text reproduced with the kind
permission of Mick Gowar, illustrations with the kind permission of Anni Axworthy c/o Sylvie Poggio Artists
Agency; 'The Stowaways' by Roger McGough, published by Kestrel Kites, Penguin Books. Copyright ©
Roger McGough 1986. Reproduced by permission of PFD (www.pfd.co.uk) on behalf of Roger McGough;
Extract 'Diary of a Skateboarding Freak', from *Diary of a Skateboarding Freak*, published by Heinemann
Library 2004. Copyright © Monkey Puzzle Media Ltd 2004. Reproduced by kind permission of Monkey
Puzzle Media; 'Ferry Sinks in Shark Hell' by Lindsay Oakley and Caroline Pook, Bella Magazine. Reprinted
with the kind permission of Bauer; Extract from 'Battle to free Wally: Whale in peril as it swims into
London', by Virginia Wheeler, Jerome Starkey and Elise Jenkins, in The Sun, Saturday January 21 2006.
Reprinted with permission of NI Syndication; Use of map text and picture 'A nose for trouble' The Daily
Telegraph, 21st January, 2006. Reprinted with permission; 'Whale in the Thames' from Daily Mail, 21st
January, 2006. Reprinted with permission of Solo Syndications London; Letter by Paulene Johnson from
Daily Telegraph 21st January 2006 reprinted with permission; Letter by Leo King from Daily Telegraph 21st
January, 2006. Reprinted with the kind permission of Leo King; 'Equal Rights' by Bernard Ashley. © Bernard
Ashley. Reprinted with kind permission of the author.

Photos: Wayne Rooney – Getty Images; Skateboarding photos (pp100–104) – Will Linford; Skateboarder
Matt Harfield – Stephen Frink Collection/Alamy; Shark – Stephen Frink Collection/Alamy.

# Contents

# Introduction for Teachers

This collection is aimed at students working between National Curriculum Levels 3 and 4. It combines short stories with a wide range of non-fiction: 15 texts in all. The accompanying activities are designed to improve the literacy skills of the target group to a point where they 'catch up' with students already working at or above Level 4.

The volume is developmental. Texts and activities are presented in three Groupings. The first of these is for students barely at Level 3, the second for students between Level 3 and Level 4, and the third for students who need to consolidate their attainment of Level 4.

All 15 texts have been recently trialled in the classroom. They are whole texts as opposed to brief extracts or 'snippets'. They have been chosen to motivate reluctant readers who need time to establish a rapport with a text rather than rehearse 'skills' by working on decontextualised passages.

The activities on each text comprise an incremental scheme of work, which teachers can use flexibly. They incorporate Reading, Writing, and Speaking and Listening tasks explicitly matched to objectives in the English Framework and in Literacy Progress Units. They have been written to suit a range of teaching contexts – mainstream English classes, small groups withdrawn for extra work on literacy, and students tackling the DfES Progress units with support teachers.

Detailed lesson frameworks and support materials for the activities are available on the Harcourt website at www.harcourt.co.uk/literature. These are integral to students' learning, and can be downloaded free of charge.

*Mike Royston*

# Grouping 1

# You Can't Bring That in Here!
## Robert Swindells

Jimmy was absolutely fed up. His mum and dad had gone off to work in America for two years, leaving him to be looked after by his grown-up brother, Osbert. Looked after! That was a laugh, for a start. Osbert had worked in a bakery, but as soon as Mum and Dad started sending money from America, he chucked his job. Nowadays he spent most of his time lying on the sofa in his vest watching telly, slurping beer straight from the can and making rude noises. He neither washed nor shaved nor did anything around the house. The place smelled awful, and the sofa looked like a tatty boat afloat on a sea of can rings, beer cans and screwed-up crisp packets.

Jimmy had to go to school, and when school was over he never had any fun. He couldn't bring his friends home because they were all scared of Osbert, and if there was something good on telly his brother always said, 'Shove off, kid – I'm watching *this*.'

He made Jimmy do all the work – shopping, cooking, cleaning, ironing, gardening – in his spare time. On cold mornings Jimmy had to sit on the lavatory to warm the seat for Osbert, and at bedtime he had to lie in his brother's freezing bed till the sheets were warmed and Osbert came to kick him out. Soon his friends stopped bothering with him, because he couldn't play out or go to football. He grew lonely and sad.

One day on his way home from school, Jimmy found a baby bird which had fallen out of its nest.

It was fluffy and cute and Jimmy felt sorry for it. 'It's all right, little bird,' he murmured. 'I'm going to take you home and look after you.'

But when he got home Osbert said, 'You can't bring that in here.'

'Why not?' asked Jimmy, dismayed.

'Birds make a mess,' said Osbert, brushing crumbs off his vest.

'Take it away. Get rid of it.'

Jimmy sniffled as he walked along the street with the nestling cupped in his hands. How could he get rid of it? If he put it down, a cat would get it.

He met an old lady. 'What have you got there?' she asked. Jimmy showed her. 'Oh, the poor wee creature,' she said. 'And are you its new mammy?' Jimmy told the old lady about Osbert and she said, 'I'll tell you what we'll do. I have a beautiful kitten at home. I'll swap you – your bird for my kitten.'

Jimmy was sure Osbert would fall for the kitten, but he didn't. 'You can't bring that in here,' he said.

'Why not?' asked Jimmy.

'Kittens make a mess,' said Osbert, throwing an empty can across the room. 'Get it out.'

Jimmy put the kitten in his pocket and went out. 'Maybe I should take you back to the old lady,' he whispered, but just then a boy from his school came along.

'Hi, Jimmy,' he said. 'What's that in your pocket?' Jimmy showed him the kitten and told him about

Osbert. 'I know,' said the boy. 'I'll take the kitten, and you can have my gerbil.'

'You can't bring that in here,' growled Osbert from the sofa. 'Gerbils throw their food around.'

'But – but. . .' stammered Jimmy.

'No buts!' roared Osbert, chucking half a pork pie at Jimmy's head. 'Get it out of here.'

Jimmy put the gerbil in his pocket and went out. It was getting dark and he was hungry. An old man was coming along the street with a puppy on a lead. 'What's up, son?' he asked, because Jimmy was crying a bit. He told the old man about the gerbil, and about Osbert. 'Well, here,' said the old man. 'Give me your gerbil and take my puppy. Nobody can resist a puppy.'

Osbert could resist a puppy. 'You can't bring that in here,' he snarled. 'Puppies wreck the place.'

'Yes, but . . .' murmured Jimmy.

'No buts!' screamed Osbert, pounding the sofa with his fist till the arm fell off. 'Get it out of here, and when you come back you can get my tea – I'm starving.'

Jimmy was starving too, but he couldn't just abandon the puppy. He trailed along the street holding the lead, wondering what to do. I could try the R.S.P.C.A., he thought. They'd look after him. But when he got to the R.S.P.C.A. it was shut. He was standing, looking at the CLOSED sign and wondering what to do, when a van drew up and a man got out. 'Oh, heck,' the man sighed. 'Closed, and I thought I'd be getting rid of him at last.'

'Who?' asked Jimmy.

'My pet,' growled the man. 'That's who.'

'Why d'you want rid of him?' Jimmy asked.

''Cause he's a gorilla,' said the man.

*Level Up*

'A gorilla?' Jimmy was amazed.

The man nodded. 'Aye. Cute and cuddly he was, when he was small, but now. . .' He led Jimmy to the back of the van. 'Look.'

Jimmy peered through the window. Inside the van sat an enormous gorilla. 'Wow!' he gasped. 'What does he eat?'

'Bananas,' said the man. 'Loads and loads of bananas.'

'And where does he sleep?'

'In my bed,' said the man. 'He kicked me out six months ago and now I have to make do with the floor.'

'I'll swap you,' offered Jimmy. 'My puppy for your gorilla.'

The man shook his head. 'You don't want a gorilla, son,' he said.

'Oh yes I do!' cried Jimmy.

Osbert was still on the sofa when Jimmy walked in, his fist buried in the gorilla's giant paw. It was dark in the room and Osbert couldn't see his brother's new pet clearly. 'You can't bring that in here,' he said.

'He isn't bringing me,' rumbled the gorilla. 'I'm bringing *him*. And you can get off that sofa – it's mine.'

Everything's changed at Jimmy's house now. The place sparkles, which isn't surprising because Osbert never stops cleaning it. He daren't stop, because Bozo the gorilla likes a tidy house, and Bozo usually gets what he wants. When Osbert isn't lugging great bagfuls of bananas from the supermarket he's sweeping, polishing, dusting and hoovering.

Jimmy's friends drop in all the time to watch TV, play video games and see Bozo. Until recently Osbert had a girlfriend, but she's left him now. She didn't like it when Osbert brought her home one evening and Bozo said, 'You can't bring that in here.'

# Wayne Rooney: England Superkid
## Gordon Kent

### New kid on the pitch

Wayne Rooney was just sixteen when he became a Premiership player. He was signed by Everton, the team he had supported all his life.

Soon people were talking about Wayne as the next England superstar.

But David Moyes – Wayne's manager at Everton – was cautious. 'Give the boy time,' he said. 'He needs to build up his fitness and learn to cope with pressures off the pitch.'

Wayne had to learn quickly. When he was seventeen years and 111 days old, he was picked to play for England by Sven-Göran Erikkson. He became the youngest player ever to represent his country.

At eighteen, Wayne was chosen to play for the England squad in Euro 2004. The eyes of the world would now be on him.

## Euro 2004: Wayne's goals

At Euro 2004, Wayne played in England's first match against France. Wayne's team were playing well – by half-time they were winning 1–0.

Towards the end of the game – in the 76th minute – Wayne was substituted. In the final minutes, Zinedine Zidane scored two goals for France. England lost 2–1.

In the next game, against Switzerland, Wayne showed what he was made of. In the 23rd minute, he scored a great goal for England. At that moment he became the youngest player to score in a European Championship.

He scored *again* in the second half. This made him the third England player to have scored two goals in a European Championship match. England won the match 3–0. Wayne, with his two goals for England, was named Man of the Match.

Wayne played in England's next match against Croatia. He played out of his skin. In the first half, he set up England's first goal. Then five minutes later he scored the team's second goal himself. In the second half, Wayne scored another incredible goal – one of the highlights of the tournament. England won 4–2. They had qualified for the quarter-finals.

## Euro 2004: Wayne's injury

Now only Portugal stood between England and a place in the semi-final. Portugal would be tough opponents, with star players like Ronaldo and Figo.

England got off to a great start with a goal in the 3rd minute. But the celebrations did not last long.

Wayne was hurt in a fierce tackle and had to be helped from the field. He had broken a bone in his foot. It was terrible news. After Wayne left the pitch, Portugal scored.

England lost the game on penalties. They were out of Euro 2004. And Wayne could only sit and watch.

## From Everton to Manchester United

Wayne came back from Euro 2004 a hero. He was the talk of England. His life from now on was going to be very different.

With a growing fortune, he could afford to buy a luxury house for himself and his fiancée Coleen, and a new house for his parents.

Everywhere he went, Wayne was recognised: driving to Everton's training pitch, going out to a club or for a meal, even walking down the streets where he had been brought up. It got so bad that he went on TV and radio to beg the fans to give him and Coleen some privacy. It made little difference. Everyone wanted him.

Would Wayne stay with Everton, or go and play for another Premiership club? In August 2004, Wayne gave his answer. He left Everton to play for Manchester United.

## Old Trafford favourite

Wayne's first game for Manchester United was in Europe. This was what he had come to Old Trafford for, and he really made the most of it.

Playing alongside Ryan Giggs, Paul Scholes and Roy Keane, Wayne was full of confidence. Manchester United beat the Turkish champions Fenerbahce 6–2. Wayne scored three times. The Old Trafford fans took Wayne to their hearts.

Now what lies ahead for Wayne Rooney? Sir Alex Ferguson describes him as 'The best young player I've seen in my career'. If he avoids injury and red cards, Wayne has the footballing world at his feet.

# The Story of Toilets
Katie Daynes

Long ago, people didn't even have
houses, so building a toilet was the last
thing on their minds.

They roamed the forests, hunting animals . . .

gathering berries . . .

and squatting behind a tree.

Then they learned to farm
the land and made themselves
homes to live in.

Some built a toilet in the yard, but it was only
a hole in the ground. When the hole filled up,
they simply covered it with mud and dug
another. This worked fine . . . until they ran
out of space.

The ancient Romans had a much better idea – public toilets. They placed a long, stone slab with holes over a deep trench. Then they decorated the toilet room with marble and mosaics.

Going to the toilet became a
great way to meet people.
Romans sat in a row, chatting
about politics and plays. Below
them, water flowed through
the trench and washed
everything away.

At Roman banquets, rich guests didn't
even have to leave the room. They simply
asked a slave to bring in a silver pot and
filled it there and then.

In later times, people were more shy about these things. Lords and ladies preferred to go alone, using fancy, cushioned toilet boxes, often hidden behind a curtain.

These were a lot more comfortable – though someone then had to empty them.

Castles and fortresses had basic toilets built into their design. Some jutted out from the main building, emptying onto the moat below.

Stinky moats were great protection. No enemy wanted to wade through them.

But the smells were about to get worse. Medieval towns were being built and everyone had forgotten the Roman public toilets. Luckily, they still had pots.

These allowed people to go in the comfort of their own bedroom. They were known as chamber pots.

But the pots had to
be emptied and the
easiest way was out
of a window.

Unlucky passers-by got a yucky
surprise. With nowhere for the
waste to drain away, the smell on the
streets was disgusting. It's a wonder
anyone ever went shopping.

Kings and queens had to
introduce toilet laws.

'I forbid you from dumping filth
in rivers or on streets,' Edward III
announced to the people of
London.

Where else can it go?

The problem was finally solved
by laying pipes and drains
underground. Toilet filth could
now glide away *under* the street,
not over it.

Of course, when something got stuck, the mess was awful.

In 1596, Sir John Harington, godson of Queen Elizabeth I, had a brainwave. 'I'll invent a toilet that flushes!'

A royal flush!

Making the flush work properly took ages. In fact, most people didn't have a flush for another 200 years.

Many plumbers worked hard to improve toilet designs, including a man named Thomas Crapper. He set up his own Crapper plumbing shops in London and took charge of the royal toilets.

By 1880, the toilet had really arrived. Since then, only the shapes and decorations have changed.

Some are fitted
into the wall . . .

. . . others are
made to look
like thrones.

Space toilets
even have bars
to stop you
from floating
away.

Today, we take toilets for granted. But spend a day in the woods and you'll soon learn how things were for our ancestors.

# Help! I've Never Had a Sleepover Before…
Janet Hoggarth

So Katie asked Jo, who asked Naomi, who asked you if your parents would let you have a sleepover. Eeeek! They've all had them and now it's your turn. You had a good time at theirs, but you have no idea how to organise your own, make it fun and make sure all your guests turn up. Or maybe you've never been to a sleepover before and you're *completely* clueless! Bingo! It's a good job you've got this book, then.

First things first: how do you decide what sort of things you want to do at the sleepover? And will they be the same things that your friends want to do? Do this simple quiz to work out a few ideas.

# What's Your Sleepover Personality?

1. On a Saturday you and your friends normally:
a. Hang out and watch TV.
b. Go stunt biking or skateboarding.
c. Pool together all your clothes and stage fashion shows.
d. Draw and paint and make stuff.

2. Your favourite type of birthday party is:
a. Going to the movies, then for a pizza.
b. One with loads of action, e.g. a pool party.
c. A fancy-dress party.
d. A trip to the 'Paint Your Own Pottery' place.

3. Would you describe you and your friends as:
a. Chilled-out chicks?
b. Thrill seekers?
c. Girlie girls?
d. Arty-crafty types?

4. You are invited to a party where everyone has to bring a game or activity. You bring:
a. Your fave DVD.
b. Twister with a blindfold.
c. Lots of make-up for makeovers.
d. Beads and elastic for funky necklaces.

5. If you were a food, what would you be?
a. Pizza.
b. Spicy Thai Curry.
c. Strawberry Cheesecake.
d. Chocolate Fondue.

Let's see what your answers say about you:

## Mostly As
You and your mates are laid-back kinda girls. Nothing too hectic for you! Your ideal sleepover would probably involve lots of food, a couple of cool movies and a mountain of popcorn. But don't miss out on other ideas – we know you would love a scary story or two as well!

## Mostly Bs
Hey, action girls! You love anything a bit daring, don't you? We can see you now at a sleepover, playing Truth or Dare and persuading people Twister is a good idea if you only use elbows and knees and blindfolds. Sit down for five minutes, though, and bask in the glory of having your hair teased into a glam style. You never know, you might like it!

## Mostly Cs
Make-up, hair products – you can't get enough. Your bedroom looks like a Boots beauty counter. Your perfect sleepover would involve transforming everyone into total babes. You'll have to smudge that perfect lipstick if you're gonna eat your pizza, though!

## Mostly Ds

You girls could make a cool handbag out of an egg box and a bit of string! You're never happier than when you are making something original or revamping old clothes. Your ideal sleepover would probably involve lots of beads, thread, glue and ribbon. Don't forget you can make food as well – get stuck into that chocolate goo!

BUT. . .

In reality, you probably like doing a combination of all the things above. And that goes for the sleepover too. You can have makeovers, jewellery-making, scary stories, movies and so on, all in the same sleepover. You just might not be able to fit them all in.

# Basic Guidelines for a Fab Sleepover

★ The number-one rule is that there are no rules! You can do anything you like. If you and your mates want to sit around dressed as extras from a scary movie watching repeats of *Scooby-Doo*, then so be it. Whatever rocks your world!

★ Sleepovers are best kept to small numbers or it can get out of control. So having your whole class over isn't really going to work. For a start – where will you all sleep? It's best to invite just your closest buddies.

★ Make sure your parents or guardians are completely happy about the sleepover and know all your plans. Ask nicely for their help. You will need them on standby to help you set up and make some of the food, as some of the recipes require hot ovens and boiling water.

★ Set a time for the party to start and have a think about which activities you are going to do. If it helps, you can write them down. They don't have to be in the right order, but it would help to have a rough idea. For example, if you were going to watch a movie, you'd want to make sure all the popcorn and food was made before so you can pig out while goggling the box.

★ If you and your friends are totally into dressing up, why not have a themed party?

★ Send out a funky invite that will have people talking and desperate to come to the sleepover.

★ Decide on the venue for the sleepover. Will it be too crowded in your bedroom for your mates? Also, you want to be able to make some noise and not creep about all night (unless you are trying to frighten someone!). Downstairs, away from the grown-ups, is usually best.

★ Do you want to decorate the sleepover room? You don't have to, but it might create a good atmosphere, especially if you're going to tell ghost stories!

★ Make sure you get everyone to bring their own bedding, sleeping bags and so on. The hostess usually bags the sofa but, as we said before, there are no rules! You can use camp beds or inflatable mattresses if you don't fancy the floor. It's not a bad idea to put down as many mattresses, cushions or beanbags as you can before everyone settles down for the night – bare floors can start to feel pretty uncomfortable in the small hours. Make sure you've got enough space for everyone to sleep!

★ Don't feel you have to do loads of activities to make it a fun night. Having too much to do will be stressy – you want to be able to chill and enjoy it. Go with the flow. If something you planned doesn't happen, it's only because everyone was having too much of a good time to fit it in!

# The Strap Box Flyer
## Paul Jennings

Hundreds of people were watching Giffen. They thought he was a bit mad. But they couldn't stop looking. He was very interesting.

Giffen went over to his truck and got out a tube of glue. On the tube it said GIFFEN'S GREAT GLUE. IT WILL STICK ANYTHING. Giffen held the glue over his head. 'This is the best glue in the world,' he said. 'It can mend anything that is broken. Who has something that is broken?'

A small boy came out the front. He held up a bow and arrow. 'My bow is broken,' he said. 'And no one can fix it.' Giffen took the bow out of the boy's hand. He put a bit of glue on the broken ends and joined them together. Then he put the arrow in the bow and shot it into the air. The people were surprised. They all clapped and cheered.

'That's nothing,' Giffen told them. 'You haven't seen anything yet.' He went over to the back of his truck where he had a big crane. It had a rope on the end of it. Giffen grabbed the rope. He put a dab of glue on the end of it. Then he put the rope on to the roof of the car. 'This glue can hold up a car,' he told the crowd. He stepped into his truck and started up the crane. The car was lifted up into the air. The only thing that held the rope on to the car was the glue.

The crowd thought this was great. No one had ever seen glue like this before. 'Now,' said Giffen, 'who wants to buy some of Giffen's Great Glue?'

The crowd rushed forward. Everyone wanted some glue. They couldn't get it quick enough. They thought it was terrific. 'Get it while it lasts,' shouted Giffen. 'Only ten dollars a tube.'

Giffen sold two hundred tubes of glue. He made two thousand dollars in one day. The customers took their glue and went home to try it out.

'You fools,' said Giffen to himself. 'You will soon find out that the glue stops working after four hours.'

2

Miss Tibbs has bought a tube of Giffen's Great Glue. She was a very old lady. She lived all on her own. Most of her friends were dead. There was no one to help her to fix things up when they got broken. So she was very glad to have the glue.

Miss Tibbs collected china. She had spent all of her life saving pieces of china. She had plates and cups and saucers from all over the world. She also had little china dolls and toy animals. She had so many pieces that she didn't know where to put them all. This is why she wanted the glue. She wanted to put up a new shelf.

As soon as she got home Miss Tibbs went and fetched a piece of wood from the shed in her back garden. Then she put some of Giffen's Great Glue along the edge of the wood and stuck it on to the wall. It worked well. The shelf was very strong.

'This is wonderful glue,' she said. 'It dries straight away.' Miss Tibbs started to put her china pieces on to the shelf. She decided to put her favourite piece out first. It was a small china horse. She had owned it for many years. It had been given to her by her father before he died. Miss Tibbs loved this horse. She put it in the best spot, right in the middle of the shelf.

After she had put all of the other pieces out Miss Tibbs sat down and had a rest. She was very tired. She fell asleep in her armchair in front of the fire.

Four hours later Miss Tibbs was woken up by a loud crash. The glue had stopped working. The shelf had fallen off the wall and all of the china pieces were smashed.

Miss Tibbs went down on to her hands and knees. She started to pick up all of the broken pieces. Then she remembered her horse. Her precious horse. She looked for it among the bits. She couldn't find it. Then she found something that made her cry. A leg and a tail and a tiny head. The horse was smashed to pieces.

Miss Tibbs cried and cried. She got her tube of Giffen's Great Glue and threw it in the fire. Then she decided that she would go and find Giffen. She would tell him that his glue was no good. She would ask him to pay for the broken china.

She hurried back to the place where Giffen had been. But he was gone. There was no sign of him. She knew that he would never come back.

## 3

Another person who bought a tube of Giffen's Great Glue was Scott Bridges. He had bought it to mend his canoe. It had broken in half.

Scott's father had told him the canoe could not be repaired. He said that its back was broken. He told Scott to take it to the tip. But now that Scott had a tube of Giffen's Great Glue he knew that he could fix it.

The canoe was down at the lake. Scott went down there on his own. He didn't tell his father where he was going. He pulled the two pieces of the canoe together, and put Giffen's Great Glue along the join.

'Great,' yelled Scott. 'It's as good as new. This glue is fantastic.' He pushed the canoe into the water and climbed in. It floated well. It didn't leak at all. Scott began to paddle out into the middle of the lake. He was very happy. And excited. He paddled off as fast as he could go.

Scott was not allowed to go out in the canoe without a life jacket. But on this day he had forgotten. All that he could think about was the canoe and Giffen's Great Glue.

It was a sunny day and the time passed quickly. Soon four hours had passed. Scott noticed that some water was starting to leak into the canoe. He decided to start paddling for home. But it was too late. The glue had come unstuck. The canoe broke in two and sank.

The water was icy cold. Scott was frightened. It was a long way to the shore. 'Help,' he screamed at the top of his voice. But no one heard him. He was the only person on the lake.

Scott started to swim to shore. After a little while he began to get tired. His legs hurt and he had a pain in his stomach. His head went under the water. He tried to get to the top. But it was no use. His lungs filled with water and he sank to the bottom of the lake.

That night when Scott did not come home his father called the police. Divers searched the lake. They found Scott's body. And the broken canoe. In the bottom of the canoe was a tube of Giffen's Great Glue.

4

Giffen was driving away in his truck. Very fast. He knew that he only had four hours to get away. Then the people who had bought the glue would start looking for him. He knew that they would be mad. He did not want them to catch him.

He decided to drive to Horsham. That was a long way off. They would not know about Giffen's Great Glue in Horsham. He could find some more suckers, and make some more money.

Two days later he arrived in Horsham. He took his truck to the centre of town. Then he put up a sign. The sign said:

TWO HUNDRED DOLLARS PRIZE
FOR ANYONE WHO CAN UNSTICK
GIFFEN'S GREAT GLUE

Soon two men arrived. They were both riding tractors. One of the men got down from his tractor. He walked over to Giffen and gave him two pieces of rope. 'Join these up with your glue,' he said. 'Then we will put it apart.'

Giffen smiled to himself. 'OK,' he said. 'I'll do it.' He put a dob of glue on the ends of the two pieces of rope. Then he joined them together. The glue stuck fast.

The men took the rope that had been joined. They tied one end to each of the tractors. Then they started the tractors up. There was a lot of smoke and noise. A crowd started to gather. Everyone thought that the glue would break. But it didn't. The wheels on the tractors sent up blue smoke. The engines roared. But still the glue held.

Then there was a loud bang. The engine of one of the tractors had stopped. The other tractor started to drag it along the road. Everyone cheered at the top of their voices.

'Now,' said Giffen, 'who will buy my great glue?'

The crowd pushed forward. Everyone wanted some. The people waved their money. They pushed and shoved. Giffen sold three hundred tubes.

At last everyone went home. Except one man. A short, bald man with a friendly smile. 'Excuse me,' he said to Giffen. 'But I wonder if you would like to buy something from me?'

'What are you selling?' said Giffen in gruff voice.

'A Strap Box Flyer. It is a small box that will make people fly.'

5

Giffen didn't believe that there was a box that could make someone fly. There was no such thing. This man was trying to fool him. Still, he was interested. It might be a new sort of trick that he could use himself, to make money from the suckers. He looked at his watch. He had to get out of this town before the glue started to come unstuck. He had four hours left. There was plenty of time to talk to the little man.

'OK,' said Giffen to the little man. 'Show me your Strap Box Flyer.'

'Not here, someone might see us. Come home with me and I will show you how it works.'

Giffen followed the little man home to his house. It was a small cottage. It was very untidy. The grass was long and some of the windows were broken. Inside there was junk everywhere. There were tools, nuts and bolts, machines and bits of wire all over the floor.

'My name is Mr Flint,' said the little man. 'But everyone calls me Flinty.'

'I'm in a hurry, Flinty,' said Giffen. 'So let me see you do some flying.'

'Very well, very well,' replied Flinty. He went over to a shelf and took down a small box. Then he lifted up the carpet and pulled out a short strap. It looked like a watch band made out of silver.

'I keep the strap in one place, and the box in another,' said Flinty. 'That's to stop anyone stealing my invention. I have to screw the box on to the strap. It won't work unless both pieces are screwed together.'

Flinty fiddled around with the box and the strap. It took a long time. About half an hour. Giffen was getting worried. He did not want to stay much longer. The crowd would be mad when they found out that the glue did not work for long. At last Flinty finished. He had screwed the box on to the strap. He put it on to his arm. It looked just like a wrist watch, only bigger.

'Now,' said Flinty. 'Watch this.' Slowly he rose up off the floor. He went up about ten centimetres.

Giffen could not believe it. His eyes nearly popped out of his head. 'How high can you go?' he asked Flinty.

'As high as I want to.' Flinty floated up to the ceiling. Then he flew around the room, just like a cloud.

Giffen knew that he had to get the Strap Box Flyer. It was worth a fortune. He could make a lot of money if he had it.

6

'Why are you showing this to me?' Giffen asked Flinty.

'Because you are a great inventor,' said Flinty. 'You have invented Giffen's Great Glue. I am an inventor too. I have invented the Strap Box Flyer. We could be partners. You could help me make the Strap Box Flyer. And I could help you to make the glue.'

Giffen did not say anything. He was thinking. He wanted the Strap Box Flyer. But he couldn't stay in Horsham. Once four hours was up his glue would stop working. The things that people had mended would start falling to bits. They would come looking for him. He could even end up in jail.

'Have you got another Strap Box Flyer?' Giffen asked.

'Yes,' said Flinty. 'I have one more. You can try it out if you want to. But first I will have to assemble it. I will have to screw the strap on to the box.'

'That will take half an hour,' said Giffen. 'I will go and get my truck. Then I will be back to try out the Strap Box Flyer myself.' Giffen went off. He had decided to steal the Strap Box Flyer. He wanted to have the truck nearby for a quick getaway.

Giffen could not believe his luck. Once he had the Strap Box Flyer he would find out how it worked. Then he would make more of them. He could sell them for thousands of dollars each. He would make a fortune. Everyone would want one.

He ran back to his truck. Then he drove to Flinty's house as fast as he could. The Strap Box Flyer was ready. There would just be time for a quick try out and then he would have to leave town.

Flinty put the Strap Box Flyer on to Giffen's arm. 'Now,' he said. 'All you have to do is to think of where you would like to fly to.'

Giffen thought that he would like to fly over to his truck. It worked. He went gently flying through the air and landed on the roof of his truck. Flinty floated over and joined him. 'Great,' said Giffen. 'Really great. How high can we go with these things?'

'As high as you like,' said Flinty. 'As high as you like.'

### 7

Giffen forgot about everything except the Strap Box Flyer. He forgot about the time. He forgot about Giffen's Great Glue and he forgot about getting out of town quickly.

'Let's go up to the clouds,' he said to Flinty. And so they flew together. High into the sky. When they looked down the people looked like tiny ants. It was wonderful to fly so high.

Time passed quickly. Hours went by. It started to get dark. Giffen decided that he would wait until it was night. Then he would be able to get away from Flinty. He would just fly off and lose Flinty in the dark. Then he would drive off in his truck and never come back. He could take the Strap Box Flyer to bits and find out how it worked. Then he could make a lot more of them. And sell them. Then he would be rich.

Flinty flew over to Giffen. 'We are very high,' he said. 'We can't go much higher than this. There will be no air to breathe.'

Giffen looked down. They were so high that he could not see the ground. They were above the clouds.

'I have only made two Strap Box Flyers so far,' said Flinty, 'and yours is the best of the two.'

'Why is that?' asked Giffen.

'Because I joined it together with Giffen's Great Glue.'

Giffen was just in time to see his Strap Box Flyer break into bits. Then he started to fall.

He screamed all the way down.

# Grouping 1: Activities

## You Can't Bring That in Here!

**1** The paragraph below sums up what happens in the story. The paragraph is not complete.

Complete it by filling in the gaps. Use **one** word to fill in gaps 1, 2, 3 and 4. For gap 5, finish the sentence.

> Jimmy's parents have gone to _____1_____.
> At home, Jimmy lives with his _____2_____
> Osbert. Jimmy would like a pet. However, when he brings any birds or animals home, Osbert becomes very _____3_____. In the end, Jimmy gets a _____4_____ called Bozo. He takes Bozo home. This gives Osbert a big shock because _____5_____.

**2** The chart below explains:

- which animals Jimmy takes home
- the order in which he gets the animals
- the reason why he gets each animal.

Make a copy of the chart. Then use information from the story to fill in the empty boxes.

| | Bird/Animal | The reason why Jimmy gets it |
|---|---|---|
| 1 | Baby bird | It has fallen out of a tree. Jimmy rescues it. |
| 2 | Kitten | An old lady gives him it. She swaps it for the baby bird. |
| 3 | ? | ? |
| 4 | ? | ? |
| 5 | Gorilla | ? |

*Level Up*

**3** The sentences below describe Osbert. The describing words in **bold** are *adjectives*.

Copy and complete each sentence. Use your knowledge of the story. This is called *providing evidence*.

• Osbert is a **lazy** person because _____.

• Osbert is a **bossy** person because_____.

• Osbert is a **selfish** person because _____.

• Osbert is a **cowardly** person because _____.

**4** At the end of the story, Bozo moves into the house where Jimmy and Osbert live. He makes Osbert do all the work.

With a partner, decide who will be Bozo and who will be Osbert. Then act out this scene:

> Bozo gives Osbert lots of jobs to do. He is never satisfied. He always wants Osbert to work harder.
>
> Osbert gets very tired. He becomes more and more cross. He starts to complain. Will he dare to refuse any of the jobs?

You can make up your scene as you go along **or** write a script before you start.

**5** Write two paragraphs about a pet **you** have, used to have or would like to have.

In the **first** paragraph, describe:

• how you got your pet      • its appearance
• looking after it          • your feelings about it.

In the **second** paragraph, tell a story about something that happened to your pet that was: funny, or sad, or strange.

# Wayne Rooney: England Superkid

**1** Read the parts of the text about 'Euro 2004'. Use information from these to fill in a copy of the Match Details below.

**France versus England**

    **Final score:** France _____ England _____

    **France's best player:** _____

**England versus Switzerland**

    **Final score:** England _____ Switzerland _____

    **Man of the Match:** _____ who scored ____ goals

**England versus Croatia**

    **Final score:** England _____ Croatia _____

    **Best goal scored by:** _____

**Portugal versus England**

    **Result:** _____ won after _____

    **Portugal's star players:** _____

    _____

**2** Read about the Portugal–England match (pages 9 to 10).

    **a** Pretend you are a TV football reporter. Check the details of the match. Then write down three questions to ask Wayne Rooney about his part in it.

    Next, pretend you are Wayne. Write down your answers to the three questions. Base them on what is in the text.

    **b** **Join up with a partner**. Act out an interview between the TV reporter and Wayne. It happens straight after the Portugal–England match. Use the questions and answers you have prepared.

    Do this interview **twice**. Take turns to act as Wayne.

**3**   Read the part of the text headed 'From Everton to Manchester United'.

   As a class, talk about what happens to Wayne when he becomes famous. Look at what the text says about how Wayne's life changes.

   Then fill in a copy of the chart below.

| When Wayne becomes famous | |
|---|---|
| **Good things** | **Bad things** |
| 1 | 1 |
| 2 | 2 |

**4**   Read about Wayne joining Manchester United (page 10). Pretend you are Wayne. Use information from the text to write two sections in your diary:

> **Section 1** is about you leaving Everton.
>
> **Section 2** is about your first game for Manchester United.

   Remember to write using 'I', 'me' and 'my'. This is called writing in the *first person*.

**5**   Imagine that **you** become famous. Write two paragraphs about what happens to you.

   In the **first** paragraph, describe getting your 'big break'.

   In the **second** paragraph, explain how fame changes your life.

# The Story of Toilets

**1** Use information from the text to write your own account of 'Toilets through the ages'.

Do this by completing the unfinished sentences in the passage below. Then write out the whole passage. Copy the spelling carefully.

**(1)** In ancient times, people hunted and farmed the land. They went to the toilet by squatting behind a tree or by _____. However, the problem with this was _____.

**(2)** The Romans invented public toilets. These were different from public toilets nowadays because

_____.

At Roman banquets the guests used _____ to relieve themselves.

**(3)** When people started to live in castles, they built toilets into them. Toilet waste went into _____. This had the advantage of _____.

**(4)** In medieval times, people had 'chamber pots' in their bedrooms. The problem with using chamber pots was that _____ . As a result, King Edward III had to _____. Underground drains helped by _____ .

**(5)** Sir John Harington was an important toilet inventor. In 1596, he thought up _____. However,

_____.

**(6)** The man who brought toilets up to date was _____. He became famous because _____. Since 1880, the toilets he designed have not changed much, except that

_____.

**2 a** A *topic sentence* tells you what the paragraph in which it comes is *mainly about*, in other words what the 'topic' of that paragraph is. The opening sentence of the passage in question 1 is an example. Write down the topic sentences of paragraphs 2, 3 and 6 from that same passage.

**b** A *connective* is a word or phrase which *links* one sentence with the next, or one clause with the next. 'However' and 'but' are examples. Write down any three connectives used in the passage in question 1.

**3** Pretend that you live during the time of King Edward III. You are walking home along Sewage Street. The contents of a chamber pot suddenly land all over you.

Write a letter to King Edward about the problem of chamber pots. Tell him:

- what happened to you in Sewage Street, and why
- your own ideas for a better form of toilet.

Remember, you are writing to a King – so your letter must be well-planned, polite and correctly set out.

**4** The modern toilet is a useful invention.

**a** Find out the history of **one** other useful invention from the list below:

- the camera
- the biro pen
- frozen foods
- bar codes
- e-mails
- the compact disc.

To find information, go on the internet and/or use reference books from the library.

**b** Then make a 4-page booklet called 'The Story of _____'. Combine illustrations and writing. Write one paragraph per page. Each paragraph should **i** begin with a topic sentence, **ii** be 3–5 sentences long and **iii** use connectives.

## Help! I've Never Had a Sleepover Before...

1  Do the quiz on pages 27–29 to find out your 'Sleepover Personality'.

Compare your answers with a friend's. Then:

a Tell each other whether you think 'what your answers say about you' (pages 28–29) is true.

b Look at the 'Mostly A's' section. Then look back at the five 'A' statements in the quiz. Explain to each other how the writer came up with the answers.

2  Read again the first section of this text as far as 'You just might not be able to fit them all in.' (pages 26–29).

The text is written for young people. The table below gives examples of phrases that show this. Fill in the right-hand column with the non-slang version of each phrase.

| Phrases aimed at young people | Non-slang version |
|---|---|
| • chilled-out chicks | |
| • fave DVD | |
| • hair teased into a glam style | |
| • total babes | |

3  Pretend you are holding your own themed party. You decide to send 'a funky invite that will have people talking and desperate to come' (page 31).

Decide what theme your party will have. Then design and write a 'funky advert' for it. You should:

- use language that makes the party sound exciting and your friends feel welcome
- use headings, different kinds of lettering, illustrations and colour. These are *presentational features*.

4  In a group, act out three short scenes for a play called 'The sleepover that went wrong':

> **Scene 1:** the sleepover gets off to a great start.
>
> **Scene 2:** something happens that starts to spoil it.
>
> **Scene 3:** the sleepover ends in total disaster.

Plan your play carefully. Have a clear idea of how and why things change for the worse. It must be realistic.

5  Read the section of the text headed 'Basic Guidelines for a Fab Sleepover' (pages 30–31).

  **a** As a class, look at the style in which this section is written. Find examples of:

  - the use of the second person ('you' and 'your')
  - the use of the present tense
  - the use of bullet points.

  Talk about why these are helpful when writing to explain something or to give advice.

  **b** Write your own 'Basic Guidelines for a Fab _____'.

  Choose **one** of the following events:

  - a Boys' Sleepover
  - a Fancy Dress Disco
  - a 12th birthday party
  - a Summer Sleep-Out.

  Write in a style like that used for the 'Fab Sleepover'.

## The Strap Box Flyer

**1** Put the following events in the order in which they happen in the story. Event one has been done for you.

| | |
|---|---|
| Scott Bridges drowns | ☐ |
| Flinty flies the Strap Box Flyer | ☐ |
| Giffen sells 200 tubes of glue | 1 |
| Two tractor drivers test out Giffen's glue | ☐ |
| Giffen first meets Flinty | ☐ |

**2** The writer wants us to feel sorry for Miss Tibbs and Scott Bridges.

  **a** As a class, re-read Sections 2 and 3 of the story.

    Then talk about **how** the writer makes us feel sorry for these two characters.

  **b** Find *quotations* from the text which make us feel sorry for them. Write them down like this:

  **Miss Tibbs:**

  Quotation 1 _____

  Quotation 2 _____

  **Scott Bridges:**

  Quotation 1 _____

  Quotation 2 _____

**3** You have invented the HEAD-OVER-HEELS MIRACLE WALKER. It allows people to walk upside down on the ceiling. It is small enough to fit into your school bag.

**a** Make a drawing of your invention. Label it to show how all the parts work.

**b** Write a description of how you tested out your invention. Include *adverbials of time* such as 'Firstly…', 'Next…', 'After that…', 'When I had put this right…' to show the sequence of events. Did everything go to plan?

**4** At the end of the story Giffen dies.

**a** Explain in your own words **why** he dies. Write this down in two or three sentences. Make sure each sentence begins with a capital letter and ends with a full stop.

**b** Some people would say that Giffen got what he deserved. As a class, discuss whether you agree with them or not. Then write down two or three reasons why you agree or disagree. Write each reason in a separate sentence, with a capital letter to start and a full stop to finish.

**5** Make up a story called 'Green for Danger'. It will have three paragraphs.

> In **paragraph 1**, you are in a market. A man is selling TRICK CHEWING GUM. He says that if you give it to your friends, they will turn green for ten minutes, then return to normal. You buy some.
>
> In **paragraph 2**, it is the end of the next day. You see your worst enemies outside school. They threaten you and demand some sweets. To stop them, you give them the TRICK CHEWING GUM.
>
> In **paragraph 3**, it is the following morning. You see your worst enemies walking to school. Their faces and hands are bright green. They come towards you, looking very angry…

In each paragraph, include some conversation. Write and set it out in the form of *direct speech*, correctly punctuated.

# Grouping 2

# The Pinballs
## Betsy Byars

One summer two boys and a girl went to a foster home to live together.

One of the boys was Harvey. He had two broken legs. He got them when he was run over by his father's new Grand Am.

The day of his accident was supposed to be one of the happiest of Harvey's life. He had written an essay on 'Why I Am Proud to Be an American', and he had won third prize. Two dollars. His father had promised to drive him to the meeting and watch him get the award. The winners and their parents were going to have their pictures taken for the newspaper.

When the time came to go, Harvey's father said, 'What are you doing in the car?' Harvey had been sitting there, waiting, for fifteen minutes. He was wearing a tie for the first time in his life. 'Get out, Harvey, I'm late as it is.'

'Get out?'

'Yes, get out.'

Harvey did not move. He sat staring straight ahead. He said, 'But this is the night I get my award. You promised you'd take me.'

'I didn't *promise*. I said I would if I could.'

'No, you promised. You said if I'd quit bugging you about it, you'd take me. You promised.' He still did not look at his father.

'Get out, Harvey.'

'No.'

'I'm telling you for the last time, Harvey. Get out.'

'Drive me to the meeting and I'll get out.'

'You'll get out when I say!' Harvey's father wanted to get to a poker game at the Elks Club, and he was already late. 'And I say you get out *now*.' With that, the father leaned over, opened the door and pushed Harvey out of the car.

Harvey landed on his knees in the grass. He jumped to his feet. He grabbed for the car door. His father locked it.

Now Harvey looked at his father. His father's face was as red as if it had been turned inside out.

Quickly Harvey ran round the front of the car to try to open the other door. When he was directly in front of the car, his father accidentally threw the car into drive instead of reverse. In that wrong gear, he pressed the accelerator, ran over Harvey and broke both his legs.

The court had taken Harvey away from his father and put him in the foster home 'until such time as the father can control his drinking and make a safe home for the boy.'

The second boy was Thomas J. He didn't know whom he belonged to. When he was two years old someone had left him in front of a farmhouse like he was an unwanted puppy. The farmhouse belonged to two old ladies, the Benson twins, who were then eighty-two years old. They were the oldest living twins in the state. Every year on their birthday they got letters of congratulation from the governor. They were exactly alike except that one's eyes, nose and mouth were a little bigger than the other's. They looked like matching salt-and-pepper pots.

Thomas J. had stayed with the twins for six years. The twins had meant to take him into town and tell the authorities, but they had kept putting it off. First it was because he was pleasant company, later because he was good help in the garden.

When the twins broke their hips at age eighty-eight, Thomas J. was discovered for the first time by the authorities. Nobody knew who he was or where he had come from. He was sent to the foster home 'until such time as his real identity can be established or permanent adoptive parents located'.

The girl was Carlie. She was as hard to crack as a coconut. She never said anything polite. When anyone asked how she was, she answered, 'What's it to you?' or 'Bug off'. Her main fun was watching television, and she threw things at people who blocked her view. Even the dog had been hit with *TV Guide* when he stepped in front of the set when Sonny and Cher were singing 'I Got You, Babe'.

Carlie had to go to the foster home because she couldn't get along with her stepfather. She had had two stepfathers, but the new one, Russell, was the worst. He was mean to everybody in the family, but especially to Carlie. He resented everything she did.

Once he had hit her so hard when she wouldn't tell him where she'd been that she had had concussion. Even with concussion she had struggled up and hit him with a frying pan. 'Nobody hits me without getting hit back,' she had said before she collapsed.

Carlie was to stay at the foster home 'until the home situation stabilises'.

'Stabilises!' Carlie had said to the social worker in charge of her case. 'What does that mean?'

'It means until your mother and your stepfather work out their problems.'

'Whoo,' Carlie said, 'that means I'll stay until I'm ready for the old folks home.'

The first thing Carlie did when she got to the foster home was pull the plastic footrest up close to the TV. 'Don't talk to me when "Young and Restless" is on,' she warned the foster mother, who was standing behind her.

'I just wanted to welcome you,' Mrs Mason said. She put one hand on Carlie's back.

Carlie shook it off. 'Welcome me during the commercials,' she said.

# The Short History of Brian Beck
## Rony Robinson

**Extract 1**

| | |
|---|---|
| **Narrator** | Brian wasn't very good at school. He was more interested in football. And pennies-up-the wall. And running. And fighting. And girls, of course. He first took an interest in a girl at the age of six and a half. Her name was Marjorie Otter. |
| | (*Ball bouncing*) |
| **Marjorie** | Let's have a kick. |
| **Brian** | No. Football's a boy's game. You're not a boy. |
| **Marjorie** | I wish I was. |
| **Brian** | Well, you're not. |
| **Marjorie** | Boys have all the fun. |
| **Brian** | They don't. |
| **Marjorie** | Yes, they do. |
| **Brian** | They don't. I know. I've got three sisters. |
| **Marjorie** | You haven't. |
| **Brian** | Yes, I have. |
| **Marjorie** | Haven't. |
| **Brian** | Have. |
| **Marjorie** | (*Raising voice*) Haven't! |
| **Brian** | (*Pushing her*) Have! Have! Have! Have! |

| | |
|---|---|
| **Miss Glatt** | Now, what's all this? Brian Beck! We don't have fighting in this school. You'd better come with me. Fighting with girls, too! |
| **Narrator** | But when Marjorie had her seventh birthday party she invited 'Master Brian Beck'. |
| **Brian** | I've got a letter! I've got a letter! A real one. Come through the door. With a stamp. Dad! Look! |
| **Father** | If it's like the letters I get, it will be a bill. Give it back to the postman. |
| **Brian** | Who's written a letter to me? Look, it says, here, my name. |
| **Father** | Open it and read it, then you will know. |
| **Brian** | I can't. Look it's a card, not a letter. What's it say? |
| **Mother** | 'Marjorie Otter invites Brian Beck to her birthday party on Saturday, June the 11th, at 4 o'clock. RSVP.' |
| **Brian** | It's from her. I'm not going to her party. |
| **Mother** | Yes, you are. This is an invitation. You have to reply. That's what RSVP means. |
| **Brian** | I don't like her! I'm not going to her party. |
| **Father** | She's got you in her grip, son. It's no use fighting women. She's caught you, I'm afraid. |
| **Brian** | I'm not going to her party. |

| | |
|---|---|
| **Narrator** | And so Brian dressed in his best red trousers and went to the party. |
| | (*Knock at the door*) |
| **Mother** | Hello, Mrs Otter. I've brought Brian. |
| **Brian** | I'm not going in there! I want to go home! |
| **Mrs Otter** | Hello, Brian. Come in. The party's just started. |
| **Brian** | I'm not going in there. |
| **Mrs Otter** | Doesn't he look nice, Mrs Beck? He's very smart, isn't he! |
| **Brian** | I'm going home. |
| **Narrator** | And when he got into the party, he joined all the others who had jammed into the kitchen to eat: |
| **John** | Strawberry mousse, with real strawberries on the top. |
| **Graham** | Mint ice cream with bits of chocolate in it, and a wafer. |
| **David** | Lemon curd sandwiches. |
| **Jennifer** | Sausages on sticks. |
| **Marjorie** | My birthday cake with candle wax all over the icing. |
| **John** | And sausage rolls. |
| **Jennifer** | And fish paste sandwiches, that nobody likes. |
| **Angela** | And mud pie! And cowpat roll! And frogspawn jelly! |

**Marjorie**         Mum, stop her. Listen to what Angela's saying. Stop her, mum!

**Narrator**         And after the food everyone played games. Angela kissed Brian in *Postman's Knock* and Marjorie hit her. Angela kissed Brian when there wasn't *Postman's Knock*. Angela told her friends that she loved Brian.

**Angela**           I love Brian.

**Narrator**         And Marjorie cried, and everyone else laughed or shouted. The boys began to fight, the girls squealed and someone was sick. Mrs Otter stopped the party and everyone went home.

                     (*A girl crying*)

**Extract 2**

                     (Brian is now ten)

**Narrator**         He got tonsilitis. And appendicitis. And toothache. And earache. And trouble at school. Trouble at school was the worst of everything he ever got. There was a new teacher called Mr Barrett. Mr Barrett hated litter, and all forms of untidiness.

**Mr Barrett**       You're ten years old, Brian Beck, and you sit there dropping paper on the floor. Look at the mess!

**Brian**            It isn't all mine, sir.

**Mr Barrett**       Isn't it, lad? It's all round your desk. Did anyone else put this litter under this lad's desk?

| | |
|---|---|
| **Boys and girls** | No, sir. |
| **Mr Barrett** | Then it must be yours, boy. |
| **Brian** | It's not, sir. Not all of it. |
| **Mr Barrett** | Then all these other boys and girls are liars? Is that what you're trying to tell me? Well, I can see I shall have to watch you, calling people liars and dropping litter! Go and sit by my desk! |
| **Narrator** | And after that first fight about litter, everything slowly got worse. |
| **Mr Barrett** | Just look at your hair, boy. What a state to come to school in! |
| **Narrator** | Brian found it hard to get anything right. His sums went wrong. And his spellings. And his writing. And even his pictures. |
| **Mr Barrett** | Just look at this disgraceful mess. All this paint and water. What a disgusting mess, lad! |
| **Brian** | Sorry, sir. |
| **Mr Barrett** | Being sorry's no good, lad, if you don't try to make things better. |
| **Brian** | No, sir. Sorry sir. |
| **Narrator** | And Brian even came to hate Mr Barrett. He had never hated anyone in all his life before. But Mr Barrett was making school terrible for him. Brian lay in bed at nights wondering how he could possibly get free from Mr Barrett. |

**Brian**           Wood shavings in his playtime tea? Polish on the soles of his shoes, so he slips? A sharpened ruler to stick in his ear?

**Narrator**        The other children took the hint from Mr Barrett. Brian Beck was not a nice boy to play with any more.

**Graham**          You're silly, Brian Beck. Not playing with you!

**Jennifer**        Ooooh. We don't want to play with a boy who's scruffy like you.

**Angela**          You smell, Brian Beck. We're not sitting next to you.

**David**           Thick as a plank of wood you are. Mr Barrett says so!

**Marjorie**        You can't do anything right, Brian Beck!

**Narrator**        When even Marjorie turned against him, Brian gave up. He decided to leave home. He packed a handkerchief and stuck it on a stick and set off for Scotland.

**Policeman**       We found your boy walking about near the station, Mrs Beck. He says he's seventeen years old and has left home.

**Mother**          He's ten. Look at him, officer, and you can see that. Now stop crying, Brian. That's not going to help.

**Policeman**       I gave him a cup of tea at the station, Mrs Beck. And a chocolate biscuit. But he kept trying to say something about a Mr Barrett. Does it make any sense to you?

# Joanne's Diary
## Joanne Gillespie

My name is Joanne Gillespie and I'm nine-and-a-half years old. I decided to write this book because, when I was frightened and not sure of myself in hospital, there was nothing for me to read. There were books for grown-ups but there were none for children. So this book is for other children who are like me, feeling frightened and ill.

It really all started with terrible headaches and sickness. The headaches started quite suddenly and they were very painful. At first, I thought my headaches were like everybody else's, but they just kept getting worse than any headaches I had ever had before. It was awful. I had the sickness most of all when I got up and did something. Sometimes the headaches were so bad, I just stayed in bed and cried with the pain.

My mam and dad got very worried. They took me to our doctor who said it was migraine because my mam and nana had it. And the doctor said it had passed through the family. We went back home and the headaches didn't get better, they just got worse and worse.

I had to be taken to the doctor yet again. This time when we were in the car my right side just went numb and I couldn't lift my right hand up to wave to a friend that I had seen. What was going on? I was frightened and I didn't know what was happening. I couldn't lift my hand up! What could be the matter with me?

When we got to the doctor I couldn't walk in – my leg had done the same thing! My dad had to carry me in. My mam and dad said to the doctor, 'This is not just migraine'. The doctor replied, 'Well, I don't know what else it could be then'. He sent me down to North Tees Hospital to have some tests.

When I got into hospital, the nurses were really nice. They asked me loads of questions like how old I was, and gave me some medicine to try to stop me being sick that tasted like chalk – yuk. It didn't work though; I was sick all over the bed. I thought I would get into trouble but the nurses were really kind about it. They put a strap on my hand with my name on. This was to get me ready to go to a different part of the hospital for a brain scan.

After the scan there was some bad news for my mam and dad. I had a tumour and a cyst. It would have to be operated on as soon as possible. The doctor who was going to operate on me was called Mr Nath. Mam and dad talked to him for ages and then told me what was wrong. They said a tumour was like a bruise that kept growing and a cyst was like a blister with water in. They said that if I didn't let the doctor operate, my arm and leg would keep going funny and I would have to stop dancing. I now know that without the operation I would have died but mam and dad were too scared to tell me that then and didn't want to scare me.

The operation lasted over four-and-a-half hours. When I woke up I had lots of wires attached to me and a drain and a bandage on my head. I was wrapped in a foil blanket and looked like a Christmas turkey ready to go into the oven. I had sticky things on me and breathing machines next to me. My mam and dad said I was shivering and twitching.

The first thing I can remember was feeling very, very hungry and I wanted to talk but I couldn't be bothered, so I just looked at things and made signs. My lips were very dry and I wanted a drink.

Later the nurses came to see me and asked me questions: 'What was my name?' 'How old was I?' 'Did I know where I was?' I told them I was in Ward 18. They were impressed. I know now they were checking my memory and speech. Then they started to tickle my feet and asked me if I could feel it. I thought the nurse was being silly, of course I could feel it, it was my head that had the operation, not my feet. They were trying to make sure I could still feel them, but I was tired and it seemed a stupid thing to do at the time.

I stayed in Intensive Care till I could go back to the Children's Ward. I had my own little room – posh, eh? All my family were waiting to see me, aunties, uncles, nana, everybody – I must have been really popular. They soon got thrown out by the nurses because there were too many in the room. Still, it felt very nice to be loved so much.

For the next few days the nurses came in about every hour to take my temperature and blood pressure and look into my eyes. I had sort of clips in my head. The clips are like staples – they're used instead of stitches and helped my head grow back together again. Some of them hurt because they had been put in tightly.

After three days the nurse started to take them out. It didn't feel very nice and she said she would only take a few out that day and come back the next day to take out the rest. Because I felt I wanted to get it over and done with, I told her to take them out all at once. So she did. Just remember to try and relax and not to cry, and it soon passes. I kept a tight hold of my mam's hand and that helped too. I was so brave I got a Bravery Award – Five Star! I'm very proud of it.

When my bandage came off, my hair was all sticky and horrible. I had a big bald patch where my head had been shaved for the operation.

* * *

I came home on May 19th. I must have been the happiest person alive. Everything was all right. We had a big Welcome Home Party in our garden. All our family and friends were invited – we had a barbecue with lots of games like knobbly knees, three-legged races, pass the parcel, and lots more. My mam made a special cake and my dad put icing on it saying 'Welcome Home Joanne'. It was a lovely day.

# The Incredible Internet
## Michael Coleman

Connecting to the Internet is to enter another world. You can 'visit' different locations, known as *web sites* (just as you might visit somebody's home) either through knowing their *web address* or by discovering them while surfing.

Let's say you want to pay an electronic visit to Queen Elizabeth II. Easy. The Queen's always at home on the Net! The address of the Royal Family's web site is:

**www.royal.gov.uk**

Zip to this site and you can tour the royal palaces, find out about the history of the royal family and much more. The address may look weird, but the different parts (the bits separated by stops) all mean something. . .

- **www** – short for world-wide web, says that this is a web site rather than any other type of site.
- **royal** – tells you the site's owner.
- **gov** – is a wider group name short for 'government', because that's what the royal family are part of. Other common group names are 'co' or 'com' for 'company'.
- **uk** – the widest group name of the lot, this says which country the web site is in. Every country in the world has its own two letter code – except for one. Because the Internet began in the USA, adding a country code to all their addresses would have been a big job. So they have a no-letter code! A web address without a country code is American.

## Serious surfing!

'Surfing the Net' – that is, jumping from one site to another as the fancy takes you – is simple. What's more, you don't get wet! It's all done by using nifty things called *hypertext links*.

These are underlined words or phrases in the page you're looking at. Click on one and it's like bouncing on a springboard. You'll jump off to another place! But remember, the net's not free. There could be big bills to pay if you use it a lot.

So, try some paper net-surfing with the game on the next page and see if you can match the web-site descriptions with the underlined words on the computer screen. Get them all right, and you're a serious surfer. All wrong . . . and you're a pathetic plunger!

# The Internet Game

**(1)** Need to send a birthday card? Use the net, there are sites that will let you design your own card. They'll then print it and put it in the post for you! In the future cards will disappear according to some people. In a survey, 43% thought they'd be sending electronic greetings by 2010. Not a lot of good if your grannie isn't on line!

**(2)** Want to know if life's as bad in other schools as it is in yours? Schools in loads of countries have their own sites. Find them by starting a search with 'schools' or 'education'. Trouble is, most of them are set up by teachers!

**(3)** The web site for the famous Kennedy Space Centre. Find out everything about NASA's space programme, and even watch a shuttle blast off, live!

(www.ksc.nasa.gov/)

**(4)** Watch a coffee plant grow! When the beans are ripe. they're used to make a cup of coffee. Does the site then become a has-bean? No. The whole thing starts again!

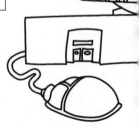

With the intern
to see the sta
shuttle. You ca
to your sch
the world. B
not free! There
bills to pay. Unles
are really go
could be le

(5) Web sites carrying news and information about major sporting events are very popular. The 1996 olympic games web site had 189 million visitors in the 17 days the games were on, and 34 million pages were read!

(6) There are hundreds of sites around devoted to pop stars, film stars, sports stars, and every other type of star. A search on the name of your favourite is about all you need.

ı can travel
hout a <u>space</u>
nd <u>greetings</u>
ends all over
ware – it's
telephone
ır parents
orts you
hout a <u>bean</u>!

(7) Want a free baseball cap or a packet of seeds? There are loads of sites crammed with information about free offers on the net. Just search 'freebies' to find out where they are.

(8) Popular TV programmes like 'Friends' are bound to have a batch of web sites and newsgroups devoted to them. What can you find out? For a start, often what happens next. Soap fans in different countries use the net to tell each other about episodes they've already seen!

Greetings: 1 School: 2 Space shuttle: 3 Bean: 4 Sports: 5

## Excellent e-mail

Yes, sending an e-mail over the Internet is that quick. No wonder regular users call letters that drop onto your door-mat 'snail-mail'!

You can send many copies of the same message to different people just as quickly. They can't say they didn't get it, either. It's often possible to arrange things so that the software sends you a note the moment your message is read!

What's more, you're not limited to simply sending words. Anything that can be stored in a computer file can be sent with your e-mail. So not only could your e-mail-pals on the other side of the world get your nifty notes, you could send them pictures, tape recordings and video clips as well!

---

### Crashing fact

To send e-mail to somebody, you need to know their e-mail address. If they have a web site, their e-mail address is often similar. For instance, the address of the President of the United States is **president@whitehouse.gov**
Test your English teachers! Ask them if 'e-mail' is a real word. If they say no, tell them it's been listed as a verb in Chambers 21st Century Dictionary since 1996.

---

## Keyboard capers

Regular e-mailers make their note-sending even faster by speeding up their typing with *TLA's* and Smileys . . .

- TLA's are Three-Letter Acronyms (an abbreviation where the first letters of the thing are combined) – like, CUL for 'see you later'

- Smileys (also known as emoticons) are groups of characters which look like a little picture when viewed sideways on – like the simplest smiley, :-) which means, 'I'm feeling happy!'

To read an e-mail packed full of TLA's and smileys takes a bit of know-how. Have you got it? See if you can put this e-mail into English!

BTW a FOAF tells me U R really 8;) HHOJ he sez :- D ISTR U said U R :-[ with a :+) and :-)> TTFN!

**Answer:**

BTW By the way a FOAF friend of a friend *tells me* UR you are *really* 8;) a gorilla. HHOJ Ha-ha, only joking *he sez* he says :-D laughing out loud. ISTR I seem to remember U *you said* UR you are :-[ a vampire *with a* :+) big nose and :-)> . a beard.

TTFN! Ta-Ta for now!

# The Amazing Talking Pig
## Mick Gowar

It was a cold autumn night on Brown's Farm. Mr
Brown, the farmer, had finished washing up his supper
things, and was just settling down in his comfy
armchair to read his library book, when there was a
gentle *Tap-tappity-tap* on the front door.

'Bother!' muttered Mr Brown, grumpily. 'I was just
getting comfortable.'

He looked at the clock on the mantelpiece: it was
half-past nine. 'Who can that be, so late?' he wondered.

Cautiously, Mr Brown opened the door and looked
out. There was no one there. He was just closing the
door when he heard a cough. Mr Brown peered out
into the darkened farmyard; there was still no one
there. He started to close the door again.

'Ah-hem, ah-*hem!*' said a voice.

It seemed to be coming from the step. Mr Brown
looked down and saw, to his astonishment, a small
pink pig.

'Hullo,' said the pig, politely.

'WAAAH!' yelled Mr Brown, staggering back.

'I said: Hullo,' repeated the pig.

'You . . . you . . . you . . . can . . .' spluttered Mr Brown.

' . . . come in?' suggested the pig. 'Thanks very
much. I will.'

And it walked past Mr Brown and into the warm cosy
sitting room.

'Wow!' exclaimed the pig, looking round the room.
'This is some sty!' It sniffed the carpet. 'And *that* is what

I call High Class Straw!'

Mr Brown tottered unsteadily into the room.

'But . . . but . . . but,' he gasped, 'you can . . . can . . .'

' . . . sit down and make myself at home?' suggested the pig. 'Ta, very much!'

With a quick spring it jumped into Mr Brown's armchair.

'*Very* nice!' said the pig, snuggling down into the cushions. 'And what's this—?'

It sniffed Mr Brown's library book, which he'd left open on the chair. 'Oooh! I see I'm just in time for a snack,' said the pig, licking its lips. 'Goody!' And it tore out a page and began chewing.

'Not bad,' said the pig thoughtfully, as it swallowed the page. 'I prefer a little warm swill, myself, but if this is all you've got in the house to eat, who am I to complain?'

'You can . . . you can . . . *talk*!' Mr Brown finally managed to stammer out.

'*Oh, brilliant!*' said the pig sarcastically. 'Of course I can talk, what do you think I am, thick or something?'

'No, no, no,' replied Mr Brown hastily. 'It's just that . . . well . . . but . . . but you've never spoken to *me* before.'

'Haven't needed to,' explained the pig. 'Everything was OK until now. Nice food, clean straw, cosy sty, good conversation with the other pigs – what more could a pig want? But tonight? *Brrr!* That sty is *not* the place to spend a cold night, I can tell you. Talk about freezing? I was colder than a penguin's bottom!

'So I said to myself? *Horatio* – that's my name, by the way – *Horatio*, I said, *this is the time of year when a pig needs a warm fire, a cup of hot cocoa, and a proper bed with plenty of warm blankets.* So here I am.'

Mr Brown shook his head in amazement.

The pig suddenly looked worried. 'You do *have* cocoa, don't you?' it asked.

'Er . . . yes . . .' replied Mr Brown.

'Great!' said the pig. 'I like two sugars. Oh, and don't let the milk boil. I can't *stand* skin on my cocoa.'

Mr Brown walked out to the kitchen like a robot in shock. He opened the fridge and, as if in a dream, he poured a pint of milk into a saucepan and put it on the hotplate.

As he waited for the milk to heat, Mr Brown tried to get used to the idea of his amazing guest.

'Fantastic!' he said to himself. 'Unbelievable! A talking pig! I've never heard of anything like it before. I'm sure it must be the only talking pig in the whole world . . .'

'Yoo-hoo! Mr Brown!' called the pig from the sitting room. 'Don't forget what I said: no skin on my cocoa, please.'

Mr Brown poured the cocoa into two cups – one for him, one for the pig. Then he had second thoughts, and poured the pig's cocoa into a bigger cup. Then he had third thoughts, and poured a large whisky into his cocoa. (He'd had a nasty shock; he needed a little something.)

'The only one in the whole world . . .' thought Mr Brown, as the whisky glugged into his cup. 'This could make me famous! I can see the headlines in all the papers: FARMER BROWN AND HIS AMAZING TALKING PIG! I'll be on radio and TV, too! That pig could make me rich! That pig could make me a millionaire! I'd better be very nice to that pig.'

'Here you are,' said Mr Brown, putting the pig's cocoa down in front of the fire. 'And if you want anything else, anything at all – just tell me . . .'

\* \* \*

By midnight, Mr Brown bitterly regretted his promise to give the pig anything it wanted. There seemed to be nothing that the pig *didn't* want. Mr Brown had never had to work so hard in all his life.

First, the pig had wanted a second cup of cocoa. Then the pig had asked for a snack.

'A *proper* one this time, please!'

So Mr Brown had made up a special warm mash to the pig's favourite recipe. The pig had sat in the armchair yelling out orders, while Mr Brown scurried frantically in the kitchen.

'Two jars of strawberry jam – large ones – and one tin of treacle. Now, crumble in sixteen Weetabix – got that?'

'Er, yes . . .' Mr Brown had replied, desperately crumbling Weetabix as fast as he could.

'Now mix up four pounds of creamed potatoes – fresh, mind, none of that powdered rubbish – and use *real* butter. Humans may not be able to tell the difference between margarine and butter, but pigs can! And when you've creamed the potatoes, add two jars of marmalade – the expensive sort, with big chunks of orange peel. Then two jars of Marmite, three pounds of stewed prunes. And finally, two tablespoons of Double Strength Madras Curry Powder – for that extra tingle, know what I mean?'

After its meal, the pig demanded a bubble bath, in the old tin tub in front of the fire.

'I can't stand cold bathrooms,' the pig had explained.

Poor Mr Brown. He'd had to run between the kitchen and the sitting room with pots and pans and kettles of hot water. Then he'd had to mix up a bubble bath using two giant containers of washing-up liquid

and a bottle of very expensive after-shave his sister Lydia had given him for his birthday.

Mr Brown was now weak with tiredness. The pig wasn't.

'Let's have some music,' said the pig. 'I see you've got a banjo. Let's have a sing-song!'

So Mr Brown played the banjo until his fingertips were sore and throbbing, while the pig sang every song that Mr Brown knew in the most awful squealing tenor voice that Mr Brown had ever heard. The pig also changed all the words so that all the songs were about pigs. Its favourite songs were: 'Old MacDonald Had A Pig' and 'All Pigs Bright And Beautiful'.

'I'm beginning to feel a little sleepy,' said the pig, when it had finished singing.

Mr Brown breathed a huge sigh of relief.

'So, time for a bed-time story – or two!' announced the pig.

Bleary-eyed and sore-throated, Mr Brown stumbled through *The Three Little Pigs* and *The Three Billy Goats Gruff* – but with the goats changed to pigs, of course.

'Well,' said the pig, eventually, 'time for bed – I mustn't miss my beauty sleep. Where's my room?'

Mr Brown led the way upstairs, and into the guest bedroom.

'Oh, dear,' said the pig, inspecting the bed. 'Tut-tut! This is no good – the bed's too narrow, and the mattress is much too lumpy. I'll have to sleep in your bed.'

Wearily, Mr Brown led the way to his own room.

'Not bad,' said the pig, snuggling under the covers. 'But still not perfect.'

'What's the matter *now?*' groaned Mr Brown.

'No hotty-totty,' replied the pig.

'No *what?*' asked Mr Brown.

'No hot-water bottle,' said the pig. 'You don't want me to catch cold, do you?'

Mr Brown staggered downstairs to fetch the hot-water bottle.

'And I forgot, I'll need a drink of water, too,' the pig said as Mr Brown came back into the room.

With a weary groan Mr Brown fetched a bowl of water.

'Now a good-night kiss . . .' said the pig, puckering its snout.

'Do I have to?' asked Mr Brown.

'Yes,' said the pig, 'you do!'

Mr Brown woke up. He was still in his armchair. The fire was out, and the morning light was glinting through a thin crack between his curtains. His library book had fallen face down on the floor at his feet. He looked at the clock on the mantelpiece: it was half-past seven.

*The pig!*

Mr Brown sat up, horrified. Then he chuckled to himself. It had all been a dream. He must have fallen asleep in his chair and dreamt the whole thing!

Mr Brown got to his feet and stretched. Then he bent down and began to rake out the cold ashes of his fire.

'WAAAAH!' yelled Mr Brown, as something wet and snout-like tapped him on the back of the neck.

'Good morning!' said the cheerful, snuffly voice behind him. 'What's for breakfast? I'm ravenous!'

# Grouping 2: Activities

## The Pinballs

1   This text is the first chapter of a novel. 'The Pinballs' are the children described in this chapter.

    a   See how many *references* you can find which show that Harvey, Thomas J. and Carlie live in America. Make a class list.

    b   Read the part of the text about Harvey and his father. Then match each adjective listed below to the character it describes. Two have been done for you.

| Adjective | Character |
|---|---|
| intelligent ──────────→ | Harvey |
| violent | Harvey |
| impatient | Harvey |
| patient | Harvey's father |
| strong-willed | Harvey's father |
| self-centred | Harvey's father |

    c   Complete the sentences below by writing *evidence* from the text into each gap.

    Harvey is intelligent because he _____.

    Harvey's father is violent. He shows this when he

    _____.

2   Read the section of the text about Thomas J.

    Thomas J's past is a mystery. The authorities decide to print a poster asking for information about him.

    Make this poster. Include in it as many facts about Thomas J. as you can find in the text.

    Set out your poster in an eye-catching way. You could use headings, a photograph, different print sizes, bullet points, bold and italic, and other *presentational features*. If possible, do it on a computer.

**3**   Read the section of the text describing Carlie.

    **a**  As a class, find three different points about Carlie's
*character*. Write them down, using a separate
sentence for each point. Add another sentence
explaining why you like **or** dislike her.

    **b**  In the next chapter of the novel, Carlie meets Harvey
and Thomas J. for the first time. Write a page from her
diary describing these meetings. It will be written in
the *first person*.

    To help you write, use your knowledge of Carlie's
character and of the way she speaks. Her diary might
begin like this:

> Some sad kid with a name like Hartley
> (I wasn't listening) came in. He was
> driving a wheel chair. I asked him to move
> it out of the way of the TV. He was slow
> with the accelerator, so I helped him by
> giving his chair a push through the patio
> doors ...

**4**   It is the first night the three children have spent at the
foster home. Use your knowledge of the text to write
thought bubbles for each of them. These will show what
their private thoughts and feelings are.

**Harvey**           **Thomas J.**           **Carlie**

# The Short History of Brian Beck

1   As a class, read aloud **Extract 1**. There are 12 characters.

   **a** First practise saying your lines in your head. When you read them aloud, put as much feeling and expression into them as you can.

   **b** Write down what you find out about the following characters' *attitudes* (thoughts and feelings) towards Brian:

      • Miss Glatt    • Mrs Otter
      • Angela       • Marjorie.

     Back up each of your points with a *quotation*, like this:

     Miss Glatt thinks Brian is badly-behaved and a bully because he picks on the girls: 'Brian Beck! We don't have fighting … Fighting with girls, too!'

2   Look again at the passage in **Extract 1**, starting where Marjorie says 'Let's have a kick' and ending where Brian says 'I'm not going to her party'.

    Write a recount of this passage in *reported speech*. This is the same style as the Narrator uses, e.g. 'But when Marjorie had her seventh birthday she invited Master Brian Beck'.

    In reported speech you use:

    • the *third person* ('he', 'they') rather than the first person ('I', 'we')
    • the *past tense* ('Brian went') rather than the present tense ('I'm not going')
    • *conjunctions* and *adverbs of time and place* to link clauses together and to build up sentences.

Your recount might begin like this:

> When he was six-and-a-half, Brian met Marjorie.
> She wanted to play football with him but Brian
> told her it was a boy's game…

**3**   Read aloud **Extract 2**. There are 9 characters.

Marjorie says, 'You can't do anything right, Brian Beck'.
Make a spidergram like the one below to show that this
could be true. One entry has been made already. Add
five more.

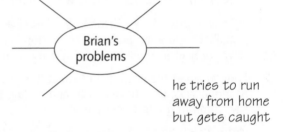

Brian's
problems

he tries to run
away from home
but gets caught

**4**   Write two scenes from a play of your own. It will be
about yourself and your friends at **different ages**.

> **Scene 1** shows you and your friends enjoying
> yourselves.
>
> **Scene 2** shows you and your friends falling out.

Set it out like 'The Short History of Brian Beck'. Before
starting, you need to decide:

- which characters you want in each scene
- how you will make clear where each scene takes place
- if you are going to have a Narrator.

Make sure that what your characters say, and the way they
speak, rings true. Then, in a group, read your play aloud.

# Joanne's Diary

**1  a** Quote sentences from Joanne's diary which show that:

- She is brave.
- She has a sense of humour.
- She appreciates her family.
- She wants to help others.

**b** Use your knowledge of the text to decide:

- What was the worst moment for Joanne?
- What was the worst moment for Joanne's parents?
- What were the nurses most worried about?
- What was the best moment for Joanne?

Write your answers in full sentences, like this:

The worst moment for Joanne was when _____.

I think this because _____.

**2**  In her diary, Joanne sometimes tells us **facts** and sometimes shares her **feelings** with us.

Read the five *quotations* below. Decide whether each one tells us a fact, a feeling, or a mixture of both. Show what you think by ticking one of the boxes alongside each quotation.

|  | Fact | Feeling | Both |
|---|---|---|---|
| **A** The operation lasted over four-and-half hours. | ☐ | ☐ | ☐ |
| **B** After the scan there was some bad news for my mam and dad; I had a tumour and a cyst. | ☐ | ☐ | ☐ |
| **C** I was wrapped in a foil blanket and looked like a Christmas turkey … | ☐ | ☐ | ☐ |
| **D** Still, it felt very nice to be loved so much. | ☐ | ☐ | ☐ |
| **E** Everything was all right. | ☐ | ☐ | ☐ |

*Level Up*

**3** On page 64, Joanne says 'Mam and dad talked to him [the doctor who was going to operate] for ages'.

Re-read the whole text. Then, with a partner **plan** to act out this conversation between the doctor and **either** Joanne's mum **or** her dad.

When planning, the person acting as the doctor should make brief notes about:

- why Joanne needs her operation urgently
- what will be done during the operation
- what Joanne will be like afterwards, if all goes well.

You will find the information you need in different parts of the text.

The person acting as Joanne's parent should write down the questions they want answered. Look in different parts of the text to find them.

When you are ready, *role-play* the conversation.

**4** Write an account of a time when **you** had to go to hospital or had an accident that needed treatment. Organise it into paragraphs that follow on clearly from 1 to 2 to 3 to 4. Plan it out like this.

| Paragraph 1 | Paragraph 2 | Paragraph 3 | Paragraph 4 |
|---|---|---|---|
| How I had my accident **or** why I had to go to hospital | The treatment I was given and how I felt when having it | ? | ? |

Write in a style like Joanne's. Try to:

- combine facts and feelings
- go into detail about what happened to you
- vary the way you build your sentences so they do not all sound the same.

## The Incredible Internet

**1**  Read the first part of this text as far as 'The Internet Game' (page 69).

**a**  Use the information about web sites to explain:

- what **www** stands for
- why a House of Commons web site will have the group name **gov**
- why web addresses in the USA have no country code
- which group name you would find in the **third** part of a Supermarket's web address.

**b**  Pretend you want to surf the Internet on your family's computer to find out about Euro Disney. Your parent or carer has a free Euro Disney leaflet. They say you ought to use that instead.

> With a partner, act out a conversation where you try to persuade your parent/carer it is better to use the Internet. You need to:
>
> - describe how you will use the Internet to find information: your parent/carer does not understand computers
> - explain the advantages of the Internet over a leaflet
> - respond to your parent/carer's arguments.

**2**  Visit **one** of the eight types of sites on pages 70–71 that interests you. Create your own text based on the subjects of one of these sites for a younger friend (8–9 years old) to read. Note: there will be some information you do not need to include.

Plan **three** paragraphs. Each should have its own topic.

Write your three paragraphs. In each one you should:

- begin with a clear *topic sentence*
- stay on the same topic throughout
- use sentences which follow on logically, one from the other.

Use mainly your own words. Add some illustrations if you wish. Do not simply download chunks of material: remember you are writing for a young reader.

**3** Read the part of the text headed 'Excellent e-mail'.

   **a** Here are the answers to five questions about it. Find the questions by searching the text. Write them down.

   ---

   **1** 1970.

   **2** This is the name given by e-mailers to the postal service.

   **3** It has been in the Dictionary for over 10 years.

   **4** They are symbols which tell the receiver what mood you are in.

   **5** I am not being serious, just joking!

   ---

   **b** Make up five more answers about e-mail of your own. Ask a partner to write down the questions that go with them.

**5** The text gives several reasons why e-mail is an excellent thing.

   **a** As a class, talk about any **disadvantages** of e-mail you can think of.

   **b** Then write two paragraphs headed 'The good and the less good things about e-mails'. Your **first** paragraph should explain their advantages. Your **second** paragraph should explain their disadvantages.

# The Amazing Talking Pig

1   Imagine that when the author Mick Gowar thought up
    this story, he made a list of what might happen in it.
    Here is the list:

> - Mr Brown is dozing in a chair when the pig knocks.
> - The pig eats a page from Mr Brown's book.
> - The pig asks for a cup of cocoa with no sugar.
> - Mr Brown makes the pig a bubble bath with some
>   bath salts he got for his birthday.
> - Mr Brown sings every song he knows to the pig.
> - The pig goes to sleep in the guest bedroom.
> - Mr Brown gives the pig a goodnight kiss.
> - It was all a dream.

Copy this list. Then put a *tick* against the things that **do**
happen. Put a *cross* against the things that **do not**.

2   On page 78, Mr Brown thinks: 'This could make me
    famous! I can see the headlines in all the papers…'

Imagine the pig stays living with Mr Brown. A week goes
by. Then the local newspaper finds out about it. You are
the reporter who visits Brown's Farm to interview the
farmer and his new lodger, Horatio.

Plan and write your front-page story. Make it look and
read like a real newspaper report.

- In the **first paragraph**, give the main facts: 'what',
  'who', 'when', 'where'. These come straight under the
  Headline.
- In the **second paragraph**, describe how and why the
  pig is 'amazing'. Give several examples.
- In the **remaining paragraphs**, tell about some of the
  adventures Mr Brown and the pig have had in the last
  week.

**3** In a good story, the author will use conversation (or *dialogue*) to show us what the characters are like and what they are feeling.

Here are two examples from 'The Amazing Talking Pig':

- 'Two jars of strawberry jam – large ones – and one tin of treacle. Now, crumble in sixteen Weetabix – got that?'

  This shows the pig is **i** greedy and **ii** bossy, without the writer having to say so.

- 'WAAH!' yelled Mr Brown. 'You … you … you … can …' spluttered Mr Brown.

  What does this show about Mr Brown's feelings? Why does the writer choose the speech verbs 'yelled' and 'spluttered'?

**a** As a class, find in the story three more examples of dialogue which tell us about the characters and their feelings. Say what they show.

**b** Write six lines of conversation – three from the pig and three from Mr Brown – that follow straight on from the end of the story. Make sure they bring out character and feeling.

**4** After another month, Mr Brown becomes desperate to get rid of the pig. He decides to put a FOR SALE advert for it in *The Farmer's Weekly*. Of course, he has to make Horatio sound like the most perfect pig in the world.

Write Mr Brown's advert. You are allowed up to 50 words. Make the language exaggerated (but not silly). Use *presentational features* such as headings, bold print, illustration, colour etc. Do it on a computer if you wish.

# Grouping 3

**The Stowaways**                          Short story

**Diary of a Skateboarding Freak**         Information

**Ferry Sinks in Shark Hell**              Autobiography

**Whale in Peril**                         Journalism

**Equal Rights**                           Short story

# The Stowaways
Roger McGough

When I lived in Liverpool, my best friend was a boy
called Midge. Kevin Midgeley was his real name, but we
called him Midge for short. And he was short, only
about three cornflake boxes high (empty ones at that).
No three ways about it. Midge was my best friend and
we had lots of things in common. Things we enjoyed
doing like . . . climbing trees, playing footy, going to the
movies, hitting each other really hard. And there were
things we didn't enjoy doing like . . . sums, washing
behind our ears, eating cabbage.

But there was one thing that really bound us
together, one thing we had in common – a love of
the sea.

In the old days (but not so long ago), the river
Mersey was far busier than it is today. Those were the
days of the great passenger liners and cargo boats.
Large ships sailed out of Liverpool for Canada, the

United States, South Africa, the West Indies, all over the world. My father had been to sea and so had all my uncles, and my grandfather. Six foot six, muscles rippling in the wind, huge hands grappling with the helm, rum-soaked and fierce as a wounded shark (and that was only my grandmother!). By the time they were twenty, most young men in this city had visited parts of the globe I can't even spell.

In my bedroom each night, I used to lie in bed (best place to lie really), I used to lie there, especially in winter, and listen to the foghorns being sounded all down the river. I could picture the ship nosing its way out of the docks into the channel and out into the Irish Sea. It was exciting. All those exotic places. All those exciting adventures.

Midge and I knew what we wanted to do when we left school . . . become sailors. A captain, an admiral, perhaps one day even a steward. Of course we were only about seven or eight at the time so we thought we'd have a long time to wait. But oddly enough, the call of the sea came sooner than we'd expected.

It was a Wednesday if I remember rightly. I never liked Wednesdays for some reason. I could never spell it for a start and it always seemed to be raining, and there were still two days to go before the weekend. Anyway, Midge and I got into trouble at school. I don't remember what for (something trivial I suppose like chewing gum in class, forgetting how to read, setting fire to the music teacher), I forget now. But we were picked on, nagged, told off and all those boring things that grown-ups get up to sometimes.

And, of course, to make matters worse, my mum and dad were in a right mood when I got home. Nothing to do with me, of course, because as you have no doubt gathered by now, I was the perfect child: clean, well-mannered, obedient . . . soft in the head. But for some reason I was clipped round the ear and sent to bed early for being childish. Childish! I ask you. I *was* a child. A child acts his age, what does he get? Wallop!

So that night in bed, I decided . . . Yes, you've guessed it. I could hear the big ships calling out to each other as they sidled out of the Mersey into the oceans beyond. The tugs leading the way like proud little guide dogs. That's it. We'd run away to sea, Midge and I. I'd tell him the good news in the morning.

The next two days just couldn't pass quickly enough for us. We had decided to begin our amazing around-the-world voyage on Saturday morning so that in case we didn't like it we would be back in time for school on Monday. As you can imagine there was a lot to think about – what clothes to take, how much food and drink. We decided on two sweaters each and wellies in case we ran into storms around Cape Horn. I read somewhere that sailors lived off rum and dry biscuits, so I poured some of my dad's into an empty pop bottle, and borrowed a handful of half-coated chocolate digestives. I also packed my lonestar capgun and Midge settled on a magnifying glass.

On Friday night we met round at his house to make the final plans. He lived with his granny and his sister, so there were no nosy parents to discover what we were up to. We hid all the stuff in the shed in the yard and arranged to meet outside his back door next morning at the crack of dawn, or sunrise – whichever came first.

Sure enough, Saturday morning, when the big finger

was on twelve and the little one was on six, Midge and I met with our little bundles under our arms and ran up the street as fast as our tiptoes could carry us.

Hardly anyone was about, and the streets were so quiet and deserted except for a few pigeons straddling home after all-night parties. It was a very strange feeling, as if we were the only people alive and the city belonged entirely to us. And soon the world would be ours as well – once we'd stowed away on a ship bound for somewhere far off and exciting.

By the time we'd got down to the Pier Head, though, a lot more people were up and about, including a policeman who eyed us suspiciously. 'Ello, Ello, Ello,' he said, 'and where are you two going so early in the morning?'

'Fishing,' I said.

'Train spotting,' said Midge and we looked at each other.

'Just so long as you're not running away to sea.'

'Oh no,' we chorused. 'Just as if.'

He winked at us. 'Off you go then, and remember to look both ways before crossing your eyes.'

We ran off and straight down on to the landing stage where a lot of ships were tied up. There was no time to lose because already quite a few were putting out to sea, their sirens blowing, the hundreds of seagulls squeaking excitedly, all tossed into the air like giant handfuls of confetti.

Then I noticed a small ship just to the left where the crew were getting ready to cast off. They were so busy doing their work that it was easy for Midge and me to slip on board unnoticed. Up the gang-plank we went and straight up on to the top deck where there was nobody around. The sailors were all busy down below, hauling in the heavy ropes and revving up the engine that turned the great propellers.

We looked around for somewhere to hide. 'I know, let's climb down the funnel,' said Midge.

'Great idea,' I said, taking the mickey. 'Or, better still, let's disguise ourselves as a pair of seagulls and perch up there on the mast.'

Then I spotted them. The lifeboats. Quick, let's climb into one of those, they'll never look in there – not unless we run into icebergs anyway.' So in we climbed, and no sooner had we covered ourselves with the tarpaulin than there was a great shuddering and the whole ship seemed to turn round on itself. We were off! Soon we'd be digging for diamonds in the Brazilian jungle or building sandcastles on a tropical island. But we had to be patient, we knew that. Those places are a long way away, it could take days, even months.

So we were patient. Very patient. Until after what seemed like hours and hours we decided to eat our rations, which I divided up equally. I gave Midge all the rum and I had all the biscuits. Looking back on it now, that probably wasn't a good idea, especially for Midge.

What with the rolling of the ship and not having had any breakfast, and the excitement, and a couple of swigs of rum – well you can guess what happened – woooorrppp! All over the place. We pulled back the sheet and decided to give ourselves up. We were too far away at sea now for the captain to turn back. The worst he could do was to clap us in irons or shiver our timbers.

We climbed down on to the deck and as Midge staggered to the nearest rail to feed the fishes, I looked out to sea hoping to catch sight of a whale, a shoal of dolphins, perhaps see the coast of America coming in to view. And what did I see? The Liver Buildings.

Anyone can make a mistake can't they? I mean, we weren't to know we'd stowed away on a ferryboat.

One that goes from Liverpool to Birkenhead and back again, toing and froing across the Mersey. We'd done four trips hidden in the lifeboat and ended up back in Liverpool. And we'd only been away about an hour and a half. 'Ah well, so much for running away to sea,' we thought as we disembarked (although disembowelled might be a better word as far as Midge was concerned). Rum? Yuck.

We got the bus home. My mum and dad were having their breakfast. 'Aye, aye,' said my dad, 'here comes the early bird. And what have you been up to then?'

'I ran away to sea,' I said.

'Mm, that's nice,' said my mum, shaking out the cornflakes. 'That's nice.'

# Diary of a Skateboarding Freak
## Ben Powell

I'm James Kitchen, but my friends call me 'Kitch' – shouting 'Kitchen!' across the skatepark sounds pretty strange. This is the story of how I got into skateboarding. The story comes from the diary I've kept ever since I first stepped on a skateboard. I made notes of all the most important moments of my skating life. My first ollie, my first day at a proper skatepark . . . even my first slam! Maybe one day when I become a famous pro skater this diary will be worth a fortune. But then again, maybe it won't . . .

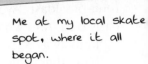

Me at my local skate spot, where it all began.

## May 7th

TRUCKS — MADE FROM STEEL WITH AN AXLE THAT IS USED TO GRIND OBJECTS. YOU CAN TIGHTEN OR LOOSEN THE TRUCKS BY ADJUSTING THE KINGPIN NUT.

DECK — MADE FROM THIN SHEETS OF MAPLE PLYWOOD GLUED TOGETHER, THEN SHAPED IN A MOULD. GRIP TAPE ON OTHER SIDE.

WHEELS — MADE FROM POLYURETHANE. MY WHEELS ARE 56MM IN DIAMETER WITH A 101A READING ON THE DUROMETER: THAT'S PRETTY HARD SO THESE WHEELS ARE REALLY FAST.

## BEGINNER DAYS

Yesterday was my fourteenth birthday, and I got my first proper board from the skater-owned shop in town. My new board is so much faster and easier to control than the old one I had been using! I'm stoked on the feeling of just riding along on this new set up. My dad agreed to take me to the local skatepark, as long as I wore my helmet. He's worried that I'm going to hurt myself, but I've got more control than he thinks. All those days pushing around on the driveway have paid off!

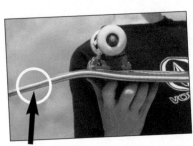

A 'KICK' AT THE FRONT (AND BACK) OF THE BOARD.

Pushing – I push with my back foot, with my front foot pointing towards the nose of my board. As I push off and begin to pick up speed I turn my front foot so that it's sideways and put my back foot back on.

## BASICS

Since my first skatepark session I've been practising basic techniques every night. One of the guys in the skate shop explained to me that it was important to make sure that I learned all of the basics before I began trying tricks. He says that a lot of younger skaters ignore them, and they end with with 'stinking style'. He must know what he's talking about: he's a really good skater!

### July 24th
### BREAKTHROUGH!

I finally learned how to ollie at the skatepark today! I was beginning to think that I'd never work it out and then all of a sudden I just did one. I've been meeting up with my friend Sam at the park every night after school. He's only been skating for a little while too, and it's much easier to learn with somebody else at the same level. We've both been watching an instructional video that explains the ollie step by step. It seems to be working!

Put your back foot on the tail with your front foot behind the front truck bolts. Crouch and pop the tail against the floor as hard as you can.

As the tail hits the ground, suck your weight upwards and drag your front foot up the board and forwards to control the ollie as you jump.

### THE HISTORY OF THE OLLIE

Alan 'Ollie' Gelfand invented the ollie in Florida, back in the late 1970s.

The ollie is the basis of all other modern tricks.

Before the ollie, skaters couldn't jump into the air without grabbing their boards.

England's Danny Wainwright holds the world record for the highest flatland ollie, with 113 cm off the flat!

## August 1st
## BARCELONA DREAMING

Got an email today from a Spanish skater my sister has met at university in Barcelona. Javier told me all about a spot called MACBA, which sounds incredible! The floor is made from marble so it's really smooth and fast. All around the building there are flat banks, blocks and stairs to skate.

Skating contests apparently draw massive crowds in Barcelona.

From: Javier Montoya
To: James Kitchen
Subject: MACBA
Date: 1/8

Hola James! Your sister tells me that you are really into skateboarding. You should come to Barcelona to visit, my friend; I would show you the many spots that are here in Barcelona. You will probably recognise most of them from skate videos and magazines. The weather is great and you are allowed to skate at places like MACBA because the artists who work there really like skateboarding. I've attached a few photographs of the place for you to look at.

## September 19th
## TECHNICAL TRICKS

Sam and I have got hold of another instructional video, which has all of the more technical tricks explained on it. We're both trying to learn kickflips at the moment, but it's really hard to get your front foot back on the board while it's flipping in the air. We managed to take photos of one attempt that worked, but most still seem to be ending in failure!

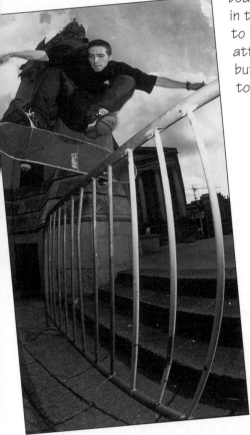

Matt Harfield: kickflip over barrier.

# Ferry Sinks in Shark Hell
## Lindsay Oakley and Caroline Pook

Lindsay Oakley and Caroline Pook were on a ferry in the Pacific Ocean, off the coast of Fiji, when it sank.

### Lindsay's story

Behind us, people were panicking and jostling for lifejackets. The cabin rapidly filled with water. The last person crawled out, and the boat rolled over. It had all happened in just three minutes.

And there we were – 23 helpless souls, bobbing around our capsized boat, miles from anywhere.

A horrible burning sensation spread over my chest and stomach, we could all feel it – petrol burns from the leaking engines.

Some people were crying. Some didn't have lifejackets – there were only 16 for 23 of us. We heaved the non-swimmers on to the upturned hull; the rest of us trod water, clinging to whatever we could.

The captain tried to reassure us. 'People will come when we don't reach Lautoka,' he said. But that wasn't the first of my concerns.

My fears were with what might be lurking beneath the surface, perhaps right at this minute. Every one of us knew these seas were infested with sharks but, like an unspoken code, no one mentioned them. So far we hadn't seen any of the dreaded tell-tale fins – but that didn't mean they hadn't seen us.

Hour after hour we clung there, freezing cold despite the intense sun. At one point, we saw a cruise liner in the distance. The captain dived into the cabin, and emerged with a flare. 'Please see us,' we all prayed, but the flare didn't go high enough. The liner glided silently away.

By 4.30pm, we knew we had to do something – it would be dark in another couple of hours and the boat was slowly, but surely, sinking. 'The nearest island is at least an hour's swim away,' said the captain. We discussed it amongst ourselves.

'I'll swim,' said an English girl I now know as Caroline. 'Me, too,' said Olivia. 'I'll stay here, to help the non-swimmers and those without lifejackets,' I said.

After much debate, 13 swam off, leaving 10 of us clinging to the upturned boat.

'See you soon, okay?' I said to Olivia. But would I ever see her again?

We watched until they were just dots on the horizon.

As night fell, the water became more choppy – waves washed over us, knocking us into the water. Each time, it became harder to climb back on to the hull.

For the first time I began to doubt we'd make it. Two more cruise ships sailed by, their lights blazing in the darkness. There was no way we'd be rescued now.

## Caroline's story

Caroline was one of the swimmers who went to get help.

After two hours I was exhausted, but we swam on. I was holding the hand of a New Zealand girl, Olivia, making sure she didn't fall behind.

'We'll be swimming in the dark soon,' I fretted as the sun set. But there was a more frightening thought lurking in the back of my mind. Night was feeding time for sharks. Would any of us survive until dawn?

We formed a huddle to rest, and clung on to each other, literally, for dear life. Our limbs screamed in protest as we struck out again into the inky darkness.

We were on the point of collapse, when someone shouted: 'What's that over there?'

In the gloom we could just make out an island. I was the first to it, hauling myself onto the rocks with my last dregs of energy. We'd been swimming a solid four hours. We all collapsed, exhausted, onto a patch of sand.

As we huddled there, trying to ignore our searing dehydration headaches, Cory said: 'You know, I saw a shark fin earlier on, just before it got dark. I thought it best not to say anything'.

'I saw it too,' said the French guy. A chill ran over my already goosebumped flesh.

We fell silent, praying for the others still clinging to the almost submerged boat.

'A light!' someone suddenly whispered. It was 3.30am and a ship's searchlight was beaming across the sea at us. I burst into tears. Had they seen us? I fished my wet torch out of my bum bag and flashed it in reply.

Shortly after dawn, the ship turned towards us.

When it came close, we recognised the faces of the people we'd left on the boat – now waving frantically. I sobbed with joy. It turned out we'd been saved by a miracle of fate – no one had been searching for us. By chance the capsized boat had drifted towards a cruiseship in the night. Passengers who heard shouts from the sea alerted the crew.

We were bedraggled and exhausted. All our possessions were sitting on the bottom of the sea – but we felt like we had the world.

# Whale in Peril

### Report 1

**A**n amazing rescue operation was mounted in the middle of London yesterday – to save a WHALE.

Marine experts fought a desperate battle to help the 18ft creature as it wallowed in the River Thames.

Thousands of spectators watched as divers, emergency boats and bare-chested volunteers tried to shepherd the lost whale back downriver towards the sea.

The whale – immediately nicknamed Wally – delighted the crowd lining both banks by surfacing and spouting jets of spray into the air.

*There were gasps and whoops as it appeared beside famous city landmarks including Tower Bridge, the London Eye and the Houses of Parliament.*

But the animal, a 'baby' about ten or 12 years old, was bleeding and clearly injured. It was also believed to be hopelessly disorientated and fears grew for its survival as night fell.

**Mystery**

Twice it 'beached' itself on the foreshore and sightings of it became less frequent, suggesting it was losing strength.

One expert said:'We will do all we can but things are not looking good for it.'

A team from the British Divers Marine Life Rescue monitored the whale as far as Chelsea.

And the International Fund for Animal Welfare sent five specialist 'whale savers', trained in marine mammal first aid, to help.

From *The Sun* 21.01.06

**Report 2**

It started as an extraordinary new tourist attraction as thousands lined the banks of the Thames yesterday to catch a glimpse of a visitor from the ocean's depths.

But by last night, rescuers were in a race against time to save the life of a 20ft northern bottlenose whale which ended up 40 miles from the open sea after it swam past the Houses of Parliament to Battersea.

The smiles and cheers of the astonished sightseers who had marvelled at the sight of the three-ton creature turned to quiet concern as onlookers realised the whale was in trouble.

News began to filter through the crowds that conservationists tracking the whale's movements feared it would die if it could not be shepherded back out to the open sea.

The whale was christened Willy by some tourists, hoping against hope for a happy ending like that of the classic children's film Free Willy.

As darkness fell, a team of divers, funded by the Daily Mail, was preparing to work through the night in the hope of loading it on to an inflatable cradle so it could be guided downstream to safety.

**'The sight was amazing'**

Without help the whale, thought to be a young male, may die of exhaustion or a heart attack brought on by stress by the end of today.

There were further concerns about the animal's condition after blood was seen seeping from a submerged wound. Tony Woodley, of the British Divers Marine Life Rescue charity, which was co-ordinating the rescue bid, said: 'This whale is unlikely to survive in these conditions for more than about 36 hours.

'It was first seen at Waterloo Bridge at about 8.30am on Friday, so realistically we need to get it into open water by Saturday night.'

An adult whale, thought to be the smaller animal's mother, was seen in the Thames estuary near Southend, 30 miles away. The younger whale was heard making clicking sounds similar to a dolphin, which may have been an attempt to communicate with its parent.

The exact reason for the whale's presence in the Thames was a mystery, but Mr Woodley said it may have gone up the river chasing a school of fish, or it may have become disorientated in the shallow waters of the Thames Estuary.

Mr Woodley said it was possible that the whale would find its own way back out to sea by following the flow of the Thames's tidal waters after high tide at around 7pm last night.

But it was more likely that it would have to be pulled back out to sea on an inflatable cradle. 'The whale beached itself on the river banks twice before high tide,' said Mr Woodley, 'but the rising waters refloated it.

'We think there is every chance it will beach itself again when the tide starts going out, which will leave it stranded.

'We will then be able to assess its condition, and if it is fit enough we will attempt to roll it on to a rubber blanket between two pontoons which will be inflated to give it buoyancy.'

From *The Daily Mail* 21.01.06

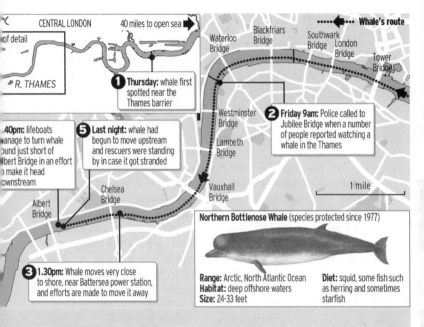

CENTRAL LONDON · 40 miles to open sea ►

of detail

R. THAMES

**1 Thursday:** whale first spotted near the Thames barrier

Waterloo Bridge · Blackfriars Bridge · Southwark Bridge · London Bridge · Tower Bridge

······◄··· Whale's route

**2 Friday 9am:** Police called to Jubilee Bridge when a number of people reported watching a whale in the Thames

Westminster Bridge

Lambeth Bridge

Vauxhall Bridge

1 mile

**40pm:** lifeboats manage to turn whale round just short of lbert Bridge in an effort o make it head ownstream

**5 Last night:** whale had begun to move upstream and rescuers were standing by in case it got stranded

Chelsea Bridge

Albert Bridge

**3 1.30pm:** Whale moves very close to shore, near Battersea power station, and efforts are made to move it away

**Northern Bottlenose Whale** (species protected since 1977)

**Range:** Arctic, North Atlantic Ocean
**Habitat:** deep offshore waters
**Size:** 24-33 feet

**Diet:** squid, some fish such as herring and sometimes starfish

# A nose for trouble

■ The northern bottlenose whale – *Hyperoodon ampullatus* – is usually found only in the cool, deep waters of the North Atlantic.

■ Studies have shown that northern bottlenoses are extremely loyal and protective, refusing to leave an injured member of their pod behind. This, coupled with a curiosity that leads them to approach boats without fear, means whole pods were easily annihilated by whale hunters in the past.

■ They are easily identified by a rounded body and bulbous forehead. Their beak-like snouts have two teeth which they use to snare squid, starfish and herring. They can stay submerged for up to one hour.

■ They can grow up to 33 feet and weigh between 5.8 and 7.5 tons, and live as long as 37 years.

## Letters to the Editor

SIR – How beautiful it was to see a whale swimming so close, how touching it was to see the brave efforts of the experts and the love of the public, yet how sad it was to see the whale die.

For two days, the tireless efforts of marine experts to save the beautiful creature gripped the nation. I even crossed London to see it, willing this long-travelling mammal to make it back out to the deep water it knew as home.

Standing by the waterside overlooking the business metropolis of Canary Wharf, I waited with a number of families, business people away from home, and workers. We fell silent in awe at the sight of this gentle giant being transported east to the mouth of the sea.

I take hope and joy from the bravery of London's unusual visiting friend. It should inspire children to learn more about the marine world, so they can see how such simple joys are so rewarding.

**Leo King**
Uxbridge, Middx

SIR – The whale was dying from the moment it wandered disorientated into the Thames, a stretch of alien water.

Separated from its family by ill health, it ended up dying while being towed behind a boat. The rescuers should have realised that they could do nothing. The poor creature should have been allowed to beach itself and die a dignified death, rather than becoming the news story for the weekend.

**Paulene Johnson**
Caterham, Surrey

# Equal Rights
## Bernard Ashley

'Can't you read?'

The man was looking at me and reaching under his counter as if he were going for his gun. He came up with another of his signs to spread over the front of a paper.

'Only two children at a time are allowed in this shop,' he read out loudly.

I looked across at the two kids in the corner. They were pretending to pick Penny Chews while they gawped at the girls in the magazines. OK, I made three, but I wasn't there for the same reason as them. Couldn't he recognise business when he saw it?

'I'm not buying,' I said, 'I've come about the job.'

He frowned at me, in between watching the boys in the corner. 'What job?' he said. He was all on edge with three of us in the shop.

'"Reliable paperboy wanted",' I told him. '"Enquire within." It's in the window. I'm enquiring within.'

'Hurry up, you two!' he shouted. And then he frowned at me again as if I was something from outer space.

'"Reliable paperboy required", that says. If I'd meant boy or girl I'd have put it on, wouldn't I? Or "paperperson"!' He did this false laugh for the benefit of a man with a briefcase standing at the counter.

'Oh,' I said disappointed. 'Only I'm reliable, that's all. I get up early with my dad, I'm never off school, and I can tell the difference between the *Sun* and the *Beano*.'

'I'm glad someone can,' the man with the briefcase said.

But the paper man didn't laugh. He was looking at me, hard.

'Where do you live?' he asked.

'Round the corner.'

'Could you start at seven?'

'Six, if you like.'

'Rain or shine, winter and summer?'

'No problem.' I stared at him, and he stared at me. He looked as if he was trying to decide whether or not to give women the vote.

'All right,' he said, 'I'll give you a chance. Start Monday. Seven o'clock, do your own marking up. Four pounds a week, plus Christmas tips. Two weeks holiday without pay…'

Now that he'd made up his mind he smiled at me, over-doing the big favour.

'Is that what the boys get?' I asked. 'Four pounds a week?'

He started unwrapping a packet of fags. 'I don't see how that concerns you. The money suits or it doesn't. Four pounds is what I said and four pounds is what I meant. Take it or leave it.' He looked at the Briefcase again, shaking his head at the cheek of the girl.

I walked back to the door. 'I'll leave it, then,' I said, 'seeing the boys get five pounds, and a week's holiday with pay.' I knew all this because Jason used to do it. 'Thanks anyway, I'll tell my dad what you said…'

I slammed out of the shop. I was mad, I can tell you. Cheap labour, he was after; thought he was on to a good thing for a minute, you could tell that.

The trouble was, I really needed a bit of money

coming in, saving for those shoes and things I wanted. There was no way I'd get them otherwise. But I wasn't going to be treated any different from the boys. I wouldn't have a shorter round or lighter papers, would I? Everything'd be the same, except the money.

I walked the long way home, thinking. It was nowhere near Guy Fawkes and Carol Singing was even further away. So that really only left car washing – and they leave the rain to wash the cars round our way.

Hearing this baby cry gave me the idea. Without thinking about it, I knocked at the door where the bawling was coming from.

The lady opened it and stared at me like you stare at double-glazing salesmen, when you're cross for being brought to the door.

'"Baby-play calling",' I said – making up the name from somewhere.

The lady said, 'Eh?' And she looked behind me to see who was pulling my strings.

'"Baby-play",' I said. 'We come and play with your baby in your own home. Keep it happy. Or walk it out – not going across main roads.'

She opened the door a bit wider. The baby crying got louder.

'How much?' she asked.

That really surprised me. I'd felt sorry about calling from the first lift of the knocker, and here she was taking me seriously.

'I don't know,' I said. 'Whatever you think…'

'Well…' She looked at me to see if she'd seen me before; to see if I was local enough to be trusted. Then I was glad I had the school jumper on, so she knew I could be traced. 'You push Bobby down the shops and get Mr Dawson's magazines, and I'll give you twenty pence. Take your time, mind.'

'All right,' I said. 'Thank you very much.'

She got this little push-chair out, and the baby came as good as gold – put its foot in the wheel a couple of times and nearly twisted its head off trying to see who I was, but I kept up the talking, and I stopped while it stared at a cat, so there wasn't any fuss.

When I got to the paper shop I took Bobby in with me.

'Afternoon,' I said, trying not to make too much of coming back. 'We've come down for Mr Dawson's papers, haven't we, Bobby?'

You should have seen the man's face.

'Mr Dawson's?' he asked, burning his finger on a match. 'Number 29?'

'Yes, please.'

'Are you…?' He nodded at Bobby and then to me as if he was making some link between us.

'That's right,' I said.

He fumbled at a pile behind him and lifted out the magazines. He laid them on the counter.

'Dawson' it said on the top. I looked at the titles to see what Mr Dawson enjoyed reading.

*Worker's Rights* was one of them. And *Trade Union Times* was the other. They had pictures on their fronts. One had two men pulling together on a rope. The other had a woman bus driver waving out of her little window. They told you the sort of man Mr Dawson was – one of those trade union people you get on television kicking up a fuss over wages, or getting cross when women are treated different to men. Just the sort of bloke I could do with on my side, I thought.

'Oh, look,' he said, with a green grin. 'I've got last month's *Pop Today* left over. You can have it if you like, with my compliments…'

'Thanks a lot,' I said. Now I saw the link in his mind. He thought I was Mr Dawson's daughter. He thought there'd be all sorts of trouble now, over me being offered wages lower than the boys.

'And about that job. Stupid of me, I'd got it wrong. What did I say – four pounds a week?'

'I think so,' I said. 'It sounded like four.'

'How daft can you get? It was those kids in the corner. Took my attention off. Of course it's five, you realise that. Have you spoken to your dad yet?'

'No, not yet.'

He stopped leaning so hard on the counter. 'Are you still interested?'

'Yes. Thank you very much.'

He came round the front and shook hands with me. 'Monday at seven,' he said. 'Don't be late…' But you could only tell he was saying it, pretending to be the big boss.

'Right.' I turned the push-chair round. 'Say ta-ta to the man, Bobby,' I said.

Bobby just stared, like at the cat.

The paper man leaned over. 'Dear little chap,' he said.

'Yeah, smashing. But Bobby's a girl, not a chap, aren't you Bobby? At least, that's what Mrs Dawson told me.'

I went out of the shop, while my new boss made this gurgling sound and knocked a pile of papers on the floor.

He'd made a show-up of himself, found out too late that I wasn't Mr Dawson's daughter.

I ran and laughed and zig-zagged Bobby along the pavement. 'Good for us! Equal rights, eh, Bobby? Equal rights!'

But Bobby's mind was all on the ride. She couldn't care less what I was shouting. All she wanted was someone to push her fast, to feel the wind on her face. Boy or girl, it was all the same to her.

# Grouping 3: Activities

## The Stowaways

1  **a** Show how well you understand the story by
       answering the five questions below.

   Write each answer in a full sentence, or sentences.
   Remember to use a capital letter to start a sentence
   and a full stop to end it.

   **i** **Two** things happened to Roger McGough that
        made him run away to sea. What were they?

   **ii** Write down **three** items Roger and Midge took with
         them for their 'around-the-world voyage'. Then
         give your own explanations of **why** they chose these.

   **iii** How did the policeman they met at the Pier Head
          know that Roger and Midge were not telling the truth?

   **iv** Why did Roger and Midge manage to get onto the
          ship without being noticed?

   **v** Explain why Roger and Midge decided to give
        themselves up.

   **b** Make up five more questions about this story. Keep a
       note of the answers. Then exchange your list of
       questions with a partner.

   Answer each other's questions. Check your answers.
   How well did you both do?

2  Look at these two frames from a storyboard of 'The
   Stowaways'.

Roger and Midge at
Midge's home on
Friday night.

Roger and Midge
at 6 o'clock on
Saturday morning.

**a** Make a blank copy of the two frames. Then do a drawing inside each frame showing the event it describes.

Write your own caption for each frame. It should explain what is happening in the story at this point. Use two sentences for each caption.

**b** Draw **three** more frames showing events that happen later. Choose events you think are important to the way the story works out. Then write their captions.

**3** As a class, look at these two descriptions from the story. Each contains a *simile*. Find them and say if you think they paint good word pictures.

- '…the tugs leading the way like little guide dogs'.
- '…the hundreds of seagulls squawking excitedly, all tossed into the air like giant handfuls of confetti'.

Talk about why writers often use similes when describing sights and sounds. Then suggest your own similes for:

- a dolphin jumping
- rain against a window pane
- a sunset
- a dentist's drill.

**4** Imagine that you and a friend run away from home. Write a story, 'The Runaways', about what happens to you.

In the **first** paragraph: **i** explain why you decided to do it and **ii** describe the preparations you and your friend made.

In the **second** and **third** paragraphs: describe **i** how you 'escaped' and **ii** some of the adventures you had.

In the **fourth** paragraph, describe what happened in the end.

# Diary of a Skateboarding Freak

**1** Read the part of the text headed 'Breakthrough' (pages 102–103).

Use information from the text to fill in the gaps below. You will need to 'read between the lines' and use your own words.

- It is easier to learn to skateboard with a friend who is learning too. This is because _____ .

- An 'ollie' is a basic skateboarding trick. It means that you _____ and then _____ .

- The ollie is named after Ollie Gelfand. The reason why all skateboarders need to learn it is that

  _____ .


**2** The text suggests a lot about James's *character*, or personality. Listed below are four things you can work out from his diary.

ambitious    popular    confident    determined

Find evidence to back up the *adjectives* (describing words) in the four clouds. Present your evidence like this:

The text shows that James is determined because

_____ .

Write as much as you like for each adjective. There is enough evidence in the text for you to produce more than one sentence. (Look at **all** the parts of the text.)

124        *Level Up*

**3**  James describes **five** 'big days' in his skateboarding life, between May 7$^{th}$ and September 19$^{th}$.

Choose any **three** of these days. Then write **two sentences** about **each** day, explaining what James achieved during it.

> **Instructions**
>
> - You will not need all the information James gives. Select the **most important** things he did on each day.
> - James writes in the *first person*: 'I persuaded dad'. Your sentences need to be in the *third person*: 'James persuaded his dad that…'.
> - James sometimes writes in the *present tense*: 'We're both trying to learn kickflips'. Your sentences need to be in the *past tense*: 'James and Sam tried to learn kickflips'.
> - If you wish, add a drawing to each explanation you write.

**4**  Choose a hobby or interest of your own. Write a four-paragraph account of how you learned (or are learning) to do it.

Call it 'Diary of a _____ Freak'.

> **Advice for planning and writing**
>
> - Your first paragraph should describe how you started. Each of the other three paragraphs should describe a new stage of learning **or** a 'big day'.
> - Write in the *first person*, like James. Make it exciting to read. Go into detail and use words that are as descriptive as you can make them.
> - Present your diary as a booklet. Make an eye-catching front cover. Include illustrations – photos, drawings, diagrams – which show why your hobby/interest means a lot to you.

# Ferry Sinks in Shark Hell

1   Read **Lindsay's story**. It shows that she was in several different kinds of danger.

    a   Fill in a copy of the note chart below to show what these dangers were. One entry has been made for you.

| Danger 1 | Danger 2 | Danger 3 | Danger 4 |
|---|---|---|---|
| Petrol leaks<br>– ferry's engine<br>– caused burns<br>to skin | | | |

    b   Write up your notes from each column into a separate sentence, making four sentences in all. Every sentence must have: **i** a *subject* and a *verb* and **ii** a capital letter at the start and a full stop at the end.

    c   Put your sentences together into a single paragraph. Its *topic sentence* will be 'After the ferry sank, Lindsay faced a number of dangers'. Useful *connectives* are 'First…', 'In addition…', 'Furthermore…', 'Worst of all was…'.

2   Find whereabouts in **Lindsay's story** the following phrases or sentences come:

- Ferry Sinks in Shark Hell
- Behind us, people were panicking and jostling for lifejackets.
- …the dreaded tell-tale fins.
- The liner glided silently away.
- We watched until they were just dots on the horizon.

As a class, talk about how each of these phrases or sentences does more than just state a fact.
What can you learn from them to improve your own descriptive writing?

**3** Read **Caroline's story**.

  **a** Make notes to show what happened to Caroline after she swam off to get help. Use a diagram, like this.

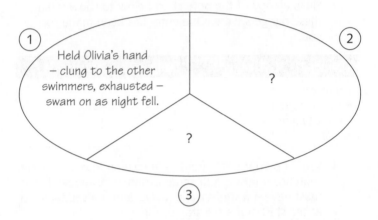

Held Olivia's hand – clung to the other swimmers, exhausted – swam on as night fell.

  **b** With a partner, decide who will be Lindsay and who will be Caroline.

  You meet up at the end of the story. Neither of you knows what happened to the other after Caroline swam off. Act out the conversation you have. Use the facts of the story but also include your **feelings** about:

  • how you survived
  • seeing each other again.

**4** Imagine **you** are involved in a disaster. It is very serious – but you survive. It could be a fire, an earthquake, a hurricane, a flood **or** an event of your own choice.

  Tell the story of what happens. Create three or four paragraphs. Write in the *first person* and the *past tense*.

  Use **Lindsay's story** as a model for your style. Try to do more than state facts. Include **detailed descriptions** so that your readers feel they are there with you as it happens.

# Whale in Peril

1 Read **Report 1** and **Report 2** on pages 110–112.

   a Compare the two reports by filling in the boxes below. Make your own enlarged copy of them first.

| Questions about the whale/reports | Report 1 | Report 2 |
|---|---|---|
| **A** How many feet long was the whale? | | |
| **B** What nickname was the whale given? | | |
| **C** Quote a phrase that shows people enjoyed the sight of the whale. | | |
| **D** Quote a phrase that shows the whale's life was in danger. | | |
| **E** Each report mentions 'a team of divers'. What did they do to help? | | |

   b Write down **three** pieces of information given in Report 2 that are *not* given in Report 1. Put each of them into a separate sentence.

2 a Read the part of the text headed 'A nose for trouble' (page 113) and look at the illustration of the Northern Bottlenose Whale above it.

   Work out the answers to these questions:

   i How did the Northern Bottlenose get its name? You need to think about **both** words.
   ii What do you think a 'pod' is?
   iii What does 'bulbous' mean?
   iv What does the verb 'snare' mean as used in this text?
   v The Northern Bottlenose is described as 'extremely loyal and protective'. Why?

   b Compare your answers with a partner's. Explain **how** you came up with your answers.

**3** Read the two letters to the Editor on page 114. The writers of the letters disagree strongly.

   **a** With a partner, decide who will take the side of Leo King and who will take the side of Paulene Johnson.

   Jot down **three** points about the whale from the letter on 'your' side of the argument. Write them on a piece of card. Then argue your case against your partner's. Try not to read aloud from your card – just glance at it quickly when you need to.

   **b** Write a short letter to the Editor of the newspaper putting forward **your** views about the whale and how it was treated. Should it have been killed? Should it have been left to die in peace? Was it right to make it into a tourist attraction?

   The purpose of your letter is to **explain** your views. It must be set out correctly. Write:

- a brief introduction
- two main paragraphs
- a brief conclusion.

**4** Use the Internet and/or reference books from the library to find out about an animal, a reptile, a bird or a fish that interests you. It can be from a species that has become extinct.

   Prepare a 3–5 minute talk about it. Then give your talk to a small group **or** to the whole class.

   Think carefully about:

- how you can grab people's attention at the start
- if you want to use illustrations in your talk
- what **tone** you want to use (e.g. serious, light-hearted, a mixture of the two)
- if you will ask for people's questions at the end.

# Equal Rights

**The questions below will help you prepare for National Curriculum tests. Answer the questions by yourself.**

**1 a** Explain why the shopkeeper says 'Can't you read?' at the start of the story. (1 mark)

    **b** What tone of voice do you imagine the shopkeeper using? (1 mark)

**2** The narrator says she will be 'reliable' at delivering papers. Write down **two** reasons why she thinks this. (2 marks)

**3** How much per week does the shopkeeper pay his paperboys? (1 mark)

**4 a** Write down one phrase from page 116 which shows the narrator is angry as she leaves the shop. (1 mark)

    **b** Explain why she is angry. (2 marks)

**5** What can you tell about Mrs Dawson's feelings from the sentence 'The lady stared… at me like you stare at a double-glazing salesman' (page 117). (1 mark)

**6** Write down **two** reasons why the shopkeeper is surprised when the narrator returns to his shop. (2 marks)

**7** Why do you think the shopkeeper is worried when he sees that Mr Dawson reads *Worker's Rights*? (2 marks)

**8** '"Oh look," he said with a green grin. "I've got last month's *Pop Today* left over. You can have it if you like, with my compliments . . ."' (page 119)

    How do you know the shopkeeper is not being sincere in this quotation? Make **two** separate points. (2 marks)

**9** The narrator laughs with pleasure when she and Bobby leave the shop (page 120). Explain why. (2 marks)

**10 a** Why do you think this story is called 'Equal Rights'? (2 marks)

   **b** Why do you think the author has chosen the story's last sentence? (1 mark)

# The best in classic and

**Jane Austen**

Elizabeth Laird

**Beverley Naidoo** Roddy Doyle

Robert Swindells

**George Orwell**

Charles Dickens

Charlotte Brontë

**Jan Mark**

Anne Fine

**Anthony Horowitz**